MIND YOUR
OWN BUSINESS

Thank you for attending the 2019 ICE and Costain Prestige Lecture.

"Embedding Learning to Eliminate Harm"

I hope the content of the lecture helps with your contribution to eliminating harm.

Regards

Darren James
Chief Operating Officer
Costain Group PLC

COSTAIN

"Managers feel baffled by the complexity of OHS systems and regulations. What this book says will come as a breath of fresh air to them.

There are so many myths to be debunked; importantly, managers really do not need to let fear of most unlikely legal consequences be a key driver of their decisions.

Given the background and credibility of the authors, managers should see this as a strong signal to look again with confidence at their leadership in safety."

Professor Andrew Hopkins, sociologist and best-selling author of *'Learning from High-Reliability Organizations'*, *'Failure to Learn'* and *'Safety, Culture and Risk'*.

Mind Your Own Business

What your MBA *should* have taught you about workplace health and safety

Andrew Sharman &
Dame Judith Hackitt DBE

Maverick Eagle Press

Published by Maverick Eagle Press.
www.maverickeaglepress.com

British Library Cataloguing in Publication Data.
A catalogue record for this book is available from the British Library.
ISBN: 978-0-9929906-9-5 (pbk)

Printed and bound in Great Britain.

Disclaimer
The material in this publication is of the nature of general comment to provoke and support deeper thought only and does not represent direct instruction or advice. It is not intended to provide specific guidance for particular circumstances and it should not be relied on as the basis for any decision to take action or not take action on any matter which it covers. To the maximum extent permitted by law, the authors and publisher disclaim all responsibility and liability to any person arising directly or indirectly from any person taking or not taking action based on the information in this publication. Sorry to add this caveat, we know you'll do the right thing anyway.

Maverick Eagle Press

ALSO AVAILABLE AS AN ebook

Contents

To the leaders who strive
to get safety *just right.*

Time and tide wait for no man.

Mark Twain, Writer

INTRODUCTION
A Few Big Bangs

The importance of health and safety in the workplace is never far from the headlines nowadays, with regular reports of things going badly wrong at different facilities around the world. Despite advances in technology and understanding the last decade or so has been littered with events that remind us that we still haven't got it right.

In 2005 an overflow of petrol at the storage plant at Buncefield, England led to the ignition of a vapour cloud, creating a massive explosion that was felt for miles around and generated a fire that devastated the surroundings. The subsequent investigation identified that a gauge for monitoring fuel volumes on one of the tanks had been sticking for several months and a high level switch for closing down the flow of petrol was inoperable. The bunds around the petrol tanks were inadequately designed and poorly maintained.

But the root cause of that incident was not faulty mechanical equipment. An independent report stated that various pressures had created a corporate culture where keeping the process operating was the primary focus and that safety did not get the attention, resources or focus that it required.

In that same year over in the United States, BP's refinery in Texas City was also the scene of a disaster when a release of flammable liquid caused a tremendous explosion and fire. The United States Chemical Safety and Hazard Investigation Board said that the root cause was organizational deficiencies at all levels of the corporation – including cost cutting, failure to invest, and production pressures – which cumulatively had impacted safety at the site.

Former US Secretary of State James Baker III led the team that investigated the safety culture and operational management within BP's American refineries. Baker's report concluded that:

"BP did not set an appropriate tone at the top or establish appropriate goals and expectations about safety performance."

BP hit the headlines again in April 2010 when an explosion on a platform in the Gulf of Mexico claimed the lives of 11 men – almost 10% of the total headcount on the Deepwater Horizon rig at the time. The blast sent a further 17 straight to hospital with serious injuries. A report published by the Centre for Catastrophic Risk Management found situations spookily similar to those noted by Baker five years earlier, noting that:

"BP's organizations and operating teams did not possess a functioning safety culture. Their system was not propelled towards the goal of managing maximum safety in all its manifestations but was rather geared towards a trip and fall compliance mentality rather than being focused on the big picture".

On April 24th, 2013 in Dhaka, Bangladesh, an eight-storey building known as Rana Plaza came crashing to the ground in the worst ever industrial accident in the garment industry. Around the world people looked on in horror as media reports poured in revealing the true extent of the disaster. The event killed 1,134 people and left more than 2,500 seriously injured. Harrowing stories of survival emerged, including those of workers and passers-by trapped by the fallen rubble choosing to amputate their own limbs in order to become free of the debris and survive their living nightmare. Several days before the collapse, workers in the building had reported cracks appearing in the walls. Whilst the banks and shops on the lower levels were evacuated, employees on upper floors were instructed by their leaders to return to their workstations and carry on as usual.

Back in the United States, on November 15th 2014 a release of 10,500 kilograms of methyl mercaptan killed four workers at the DuPont chemical plant in LaPorte, Texas. The chemical is used to produce insecticides and fungicides and as an additive to give natural gas that typical 'rotten egg' smell. During the release, the smell could be detected up to 40 miles away. Whilst accurate reports on the details of the accident are hard to find, it's understood that when one worker was overcome by the chemical others went to her aid and ultimately succumbed to the gas. DuPont, previously regarded by many as one of the world's safest companies was charged with several violations under American safety legislation leading the Chairman of the U.S. Chemical Safety Board, Rafael Moure-Erasmo to remark:

"What we are seeing here in this incident in LaPorte is definitely a problem of safety culture in the corporation of DuPont."

And it's not all about industrial operations. On the 2nd June 2015 four people suffered horrific life-changing injuries – two sustaining amputated legs – at Alton Towers theme park in the United Kingdom when two rollercoaster carriages collided. Young people enjoying a day out – which should have been great fun – found themselves living a nightmare. By the end of that year, a Google search returns almost 350,000 news items related to the accident at Alton Towers and bosses announced that decreased Summer revenues, in the wake of the accident, had contributed to 190 redundancies in 2015.

Over a year later, in September 2016 the company behind Alton Towers, Merlin Attractions Operations Ltd, was fined £5 million. In September 2016 even the most cursory internet search returns over 300,000 hits, proving that the memory of the event is still very much alive whilst Merlin Entertainment reports the £14 million drop in revenue the park endured as a result of the crash.

Merlin Attractions was fined after the court heard that an engineer *"felt pressure"* to get the 'Smiler' rollercoaster back into service after it developed a fault shortly before the devastating crash. During the hearing, an expert witness report reported that Alton Towers management linked bonuses to *"acceptably low levels of downtime"* on their rollercoasters.

Judge Michael Chambers QC called the accident a *"catastrophic failure"* by the company and leaders involved stating that this was *"a needless and avoidable accident in which those injured were fortunate not to have been killed or bled to death."* Judge Chambers said the *"obvious shambles of what occurred"* could have been *"easily avoided"* by the leaders ensuring a suitable written system to deal with ride faults and a proper risk assessment. The judge added that the injured *"endured great pain and distress"* whilst waiting for medical help, with the first 999 call not made until seventeen minutes after the crash. It took up to five hours for the injured persons to be freed from the wreckage.

Judge Chambers stated that all sixteen people aboard the carriage had been *"injured to various degrees"* adding that the company's safety failures had been *"putting at risk the safety of thousands of young people and children"*. Beginning sentencing, he said *"The defendant now accepts the prosecution case that the underlying fault was 'an absence of a structured and considered system' not that of individuals' efforts, doing their best within a flawed system."*

Less than two months after the Alton Towers prosecution an even more tragic incident occurred at another theme park, this time at Dreamland in Queensland, Australia, where four people lost their lives. This time the entertainment involved was a river rapids ride, not a roller-coaster, but it was yet another incident that non-one thought could happen. But it did.

The headlines from events like those outlined above resonate with us all as leaders, as human beings. And there's many, many more that have occurred in our recent past: Flixborough, Challenger, Columbia, Virgin Galactic, Aberfan, Ocean Ranger, Fukushima, Chernobyl, Bhopal, MS Estonia, Costa Concordia, Kings Cross, Coalbrook, PanAm flight 1736, American Airlines flight 587, Piper Alpha, Bradford City, Summerland. The list goes on and on. For each and every one, several common threads continue to emerge: leadership, management, culture. Each time the headlines break, businesspeople around the world suck in their breath and vow *"it'll never happen to me."* It may be that the nature of *your* business is such that disasters of this scale may never happen to you, but it is a stark fact that each and every day organizations just like yours right around the globe are experiencing accidents that whilst they don't necessarily hit the front pages of the papers they certainly change the lives of people. People just like you.

Is good safety good business?

The International Labor Organization reports that there are around 2.3 million deaths per year around the world as a result of workplace accidents or work-related diseases. That's a global average of 13 fatalities among every 100,000 employees. In developed countries the rate lies between 0.5 and 3.5 deaths per 100,000 workers whilst emerging economies, such as sub-Saharan Africa, Latin America and Southern Asia the rate rises sharply to up to 19 per 100,000.

Beyond the human tragedy the economic cost of accidents is significant too. The ILO put the average cost of workplace accidents at around 4% of global Gross Domestic Product. In real terms that's about 2.8 trillion US dollars. Detailed studies reveal Singapore's accident costs were equivalent to 3.2% of the country's GDP. In Italy it's the same rate. In Australia it jumps to 5.9%, or around 57.5 billion Australian dollars. And if involuntary retirement due to work-related accident or ill-health is factored in then costs would be considerably higher – for example, as much as up to 15% of the GDP in Finland.

In the Great Britain, workplace safety regulator the Health & Safety Executive calculates that the annual cost to society of accidents, injuries and work-related ill-health is £13.8 billion. This figure impacts individuals to the tune of £8 billion, whilst employers and the UK government bear the brunt of around £6 Billion each.

The phrase 'good safety is good business' has been trotted out glibly in recent years. But is the maxim true? In 2013, the World Economic Forum examined whether there really was a link. The Forum found that organizational competitiveness and workplace health and safety do go hand-in-hand: in simple terms the data confirms that the lower the number of accidents, the higher the organization's competitiveness and productivity. Evidence from countries including Switzerland, Finland, Singapore, the Netherlands, Germany, Japan, Canada, Belgium, Sweden, the UK and the USA all positively proved the point; that good safety really is measurably good for business.

Whichever way you slice it, addressing issues of workplace safety and health is a vital aspect of doing business today, wherever in the world you are. It has to be an integral part of running the business, not something that is done by others or which you do because someone else tells you that you have to. We believe that minding your own business when it comes to safety is key. Recent studies reveal that clear, supportive leadership; good management; effective worker engagement; and systems thinking at all levels are core components for building a culture where the health and safety of workers is valued, protected, and in many cases, even enhanced. It matters not whether your organization is an SME battling through your first few years or a massive scale construction such as the London 2012 Olympics. Success, as the Olympics project (and many others we know well) confirmed is built through the emphasis on and continuous follow-up of these factors.

The times they are a'changing

In many countries around the world government regulators responsible for enforcing safety laws are raising their game. Historically, penalties for workplace safety failings would be applied to the corporation and although safety regulations in many countries provide for personal prosecution of responsible managers and leaders, only rarely has this happened in practice. But over the last few years in the United Kingdom this has all changed. In the twelve months from April 2015 to March 2016 46 company directors and managers were prosecuted by the Health & Safety Executive. Of these, 34 were found guilty and

12 were given prison sentences of up to two years. What we're seeing is an increased focus by the regulatory body to prosecute the most senior leaders within an organization. This makes good sense, by holding senior management responsible for the safety failings of their companies, the increasing enforcement is starting to push more robust discussion on safety onto boardroom tables.

Further, new court guidelines, released in February 2016, on sentencing for safety failings are also changing the game. In the last year in the UK the total value of fines imposed for safety offences has risen 43 percent over the previous year. As an example, between February 2016 and August 2016 health and safety fines in the UK totalled £20.6 million, compared to £14.6 million across the same period in 2015. We think that this figure is conservative, given that in some businesses – such as offices, shops and other retail premises – workplace safety laws are enforced by Local Authorities rather than the HSE. But let's look at the value of the penalties in detail. In the last few months there have been some very high value, high profile fines including:

- Railway operator Network Rail fined £4 million for the death of an elderly lady at a railway crossing

- A £1.6 million fine for Foodles Production company after Hollywood A-lister Harrison Ford was injured on the Star Wars film set

- Amusement park operator Merlin Entertainments was fined £5 million after a rollercoaster crash left two young women with amputated legs

It would appear that after years of relatively stable (and arguably low impact) penalties the times are indeed changing as these new sentencing guidelines are being rigorously applied by the criminal courts.

We think that company directors should be feeling more than a little concerned by this change, especially given that fines are now regularly hitting the £1 million mark for non-fatal accidents. Breaches of health and safety laws are becoming more and more a serious threat to the corporate bottom line and heavy fines will likely extend to workplace accidents where no injuries are sustained. And as the guidelines encourage judges to consider revenue, if your organization has a turnover of £50 million or more, this could mean a penalty in the region of £100 million for a serious accident.

We think it's high time for business leaders – not just those in charge of operations, but also CFOs, Accountants, and Directors – both Executive and Non-Executive – to sit up and take note. And action.

The health & safety leadership paradox

The belief that leaders are 'born rather than made' seems to have fallen out of favour. In the last few years business schools around the world have been reporting a boom in Masters of Business Administration (MBA) programs. In the UK, Oxford University's Said Business School report that their 2015 MBA student intake was up 50% on the previous year. Warwick Business School's popularity with MBA students has encouraged a £30 million state-of-the-art extension to its current facilities and the acquisition of an entire floor in Europe's tallest building, The Shard, in London. INSEAD, IMD, Judge, Cranfield, Harvard, London Business School, Wharton, Yale, Stanford, Columbia, – all featuring in the various 'top tens' of business schools across the world, alongside Said and Warwick – all report healthy increases in their MBA cohorts – most seeing double-digit percentage increases year-on-year.

Back in 1988, American academic researchers Porter and McKibbin suggested that business school graduates are not considered by the business community to be sufficiently prepared for life in the real world of corporate life. The good doctors slammed Universities for not equipping their students with the skills required and recommended that the teaching of interpersonal skills – including communication and leadership – be incorporated into business school curricula.

The academics were way ahead of their time. Since their report, the increasingly complex global business environment makes skills such as the ability to understand employee, customer, and team diversities and operate effectively within them even more vital to management education.

Independent organizational surveys conducted over the last decade continue to confirm that a range of skills and attributes are important to employers when hiring graduates. These skills include verbal and non-verbal communication, active-listening, building and maintaining interpersonal relationships, team-building, leadership and supervision, analysis and decision-making. The surveys point to the necessity of practical education and to the up-skilling of learners to support them in their readiness for the real world.

Empty MBAs?

In this book we argue that workplace health and safety sits firmly in the real world of work and therefore needs to be part of preparing managers to become leaders in the real world. Our review of MBA programs around the globe, however, reveals very, very few that include the topic. One notable exception comes from Canada, where the University of Fredericton has made the bold step of *creating* an Executive MBA with a deep focus on Health & Safety Leadership. The Fredericton Executive MBA is designed for business professionals who aspire to lead their businesses towards much higher performance. As you'd expect, it commences with broad coverage of foundational management essentials including financial, analytical and decision-making skills, and developing knowledge of an organization's core functions and interactions. The program then dives much deeper. Its core focus is on leadership *techniques*, especially collaborative leadership in the complex context of multiple stakeholders and multiple objectives; then it augments this core focus with a series of specialty stream courses focused exclusively on the needs of health and safety leaders.

Developed in collaboration with the national professional body for safety practitioners, the Canadian Society of Safety Engineering (CSSE), Fredericton believes that:

"The role of the health and safety unit in an organization has been steadily and significantly rising in prominence over the last several decades. This is well-deserved, as the evidence clearly indicates that well-designed and well-managed health and safety programs contribute to a much healthier, more satisfied and more productive workforce, coincidentally with a significant financial upside for the organization."

The University points out that many managers of health and safety departments have reached their leadership positions without any prior higher education in management and thus face *"the dual challenges of a potential performance deficit, and reduced probability of promotion into executive ranks"*. In our dialogue with the University smiles crept over our faces as we hear a version of a familiar old mantra *'If we always see things the way we've always seen them, we'll always do what we've always done.'*

Fredericton takes a fresh approach: their goal is to upskill advanced-career professionals and managers for senior managerial positions and to prepare them for success in those positions, without interrupting their career momentum, or in their words:

"What we need to do in executive leadership is give MBA students lots of tools to help them do stuff in safety effectively."

The MBA program, running since 2007, now boasts an annual intake of around 60 managers and cohort size has doubled year on year in recent times. Something's obviously working well.

Over the last few years, perched on the edge of the magnificent Fontainebleau forest, an hour south of Paris someone has noticed a gap in the market. The *Centre Europeen d'Education Permanante* ('CEDEP' for short, or the European Centre for Executive Development, in English) offers a one-week intensive residential program, on the campus of leading global business school INSEAD, where leadership and safety culture are the order of the day, every day. Program Director Professor Sam Abadir passionately argues that:

"It's the responsibility of senior leaders to create a culture of safety. Technical managers are supposed to build safe systems, whilst middle managers are in charge of promoting safe behaviour."

But a commitment to safety is not just part of the job description. Most management experts agree that leaders who demonstrate commitment to their team's wellbeing inspire greater motivation and thus get teams to produce better work faster. In other words, paying attention to safety makes you a better leader and fosters better business. CEDEP's innovative safety and leadership program helps leaders from all sectors to rise to the many challenges involved in creating a robust organizational safety culture that really does lead to high performance. And with a waiting list of leaders from multi-national blue-chip corporates, it looks like Professor Abadir is absolutely right.

So if Fredericton and CEDEP have seen the light and are experiencing year-on-year increased demand for their programs, why don't other MBA schools and executive development programs include safety in their syllabus?

Because safety isn't sexy? Well, we would argue that it can be.

Because safety isn't important? We can't believe that any university worth its salt would think this.

Because safety isn't for top tier leaders? We strongly disagree.

Because safety is too difficult? We say it doesn't have to be.

Getting the balance *just right*

The book you hold in your hands right now seeks to address the gaps within current MBA programs and other executive learning with regard to workplace health and safety. To *see differently* we have to be *be* different. It's not about doing everything differently or just seeing things from a new perspective. It begins with *thinking* differently.

In these pages we'll help you to recast your relationships with experts in health and safety. To differentiate between those over-zealous 'technical experts' who over-prescribe and over-regulate your business affairs and to help you spot, support and collaborate with those best-in-class safety practitioners that can really help you in your organization. We'll demonstrate why a difference of opinion and perspective in health and safety is not just useful but indeed essential to success – in safety and in business more broadly. We'll make the distinction between advice and decision-taking and argue that there really isn't one right way to guarantee success in safety at work. We will explain why it has to be *just right* for you and your organization. But we will also show you that it's not as difficult as you may have believed (or have been led to believe). Finally, and as a central theme running throughout this entire book, we'll explain just why health and safety needs to be an integral part of *your* job as a manager or leader, rather than something to be left only to the specialists. Oh, and we'll also motivate you to see it as leading for success not simply avoiding failure.

We will reflect and share what we have learned in the hope that you will be inspired to look again at health and safety with a fresh outlook and seize the opportunity to make it an integral part of your leadership. Amongst the big issues we'll consider in this book are:

- What creates the right safety culture? Does focusing on the small stuff like lids on coffee cups and holding the handrails really lead to high performance or deep cynicism?

- How to put legal requirements into perspective whilst avoiding them becoming the main driver for what you do

- Differentiating between failures in criminal law and civil liability and identifying why an obsession with the latter creates a culture which stifles everyone

- How to choose and use the right tools to manage risk – and recognising the difference between a menu of risk controls and a must-do check list

- Identifying and cultivating a safety leadership style which is right for you and for the business you are leading

- Knowing when to call on expertise and how to use that knowledge effectively and proportionately

- Creating a culture where everyone in your organization knows their responsibilities and is comfortable with taking on personal responsibility

A route map for action

This book is presented to you in five parts, each one designed to build on the previous section. At the end of each chapter we present a number of reflection points for you to consider, together with suggestions for specific actions that will demonstrate your leadership in safety.

We begin by setting context and examining the global world of work in which we operate, and in which, when it comes to health and safety, myths abound. In chapter one we'll explore why the world today has become so risk averse. Society – with more than a little help from the media – has brought about a particularly negative view, but what really lies behind the many ridiculous stories of innocuous activities banned in the name of health and safety?

When it comes to the workplace, why have we handed over health and safety to a team of so called 'experts' rather than owning it and managing it ourselves as business leaders? Is it because 'they' have told us it's so complex we can't possibly understand, let alone do it? Or are we afraid of something or someone – and if so what? Where and how did we become addicted to management systems and paperwork and lose sight of the human part of managing?

We'll consider whether it is possible to row back from the age of entitlement and the prevailing blame culture and try to work out just why some people seek to put the blame on someone else rather than taking ownership and responsibility themselves.

In chapter two we'll explain that we live in a world where we have more freedom and choice than ever before, and in an age where independence and opinion are the currencies of modern life. So why is it that we seem to want to defer to a 'do as you're told' mindset when it comes to health and safety? What is it that we are afraid of? Why do we lack the confidence to lead and manage when it comes to health and safety?

In no other field of management would the leader ever step aside and let someone else tell them how to run their business, but managers do that all the time when it comes to the business of health and safety. Why is this? What's the worst that could happen? In this chapter we'll explain how managers can – and why they should – take ownership for leading this vitally important aspect of their business.

Complex attitudes live in every boardroom and create the environment where leaders take the decisions they do. In chapter three we'll explore why discussions and decisions on matters of safety are so difficult. We argue that fear of failure is a key element but we'll advance that it's more than the only factor at play. It's also about a fundamental lack of knowledge on what to do and how to do it.

Management systems have grown in popularity and use. Despite the many advantages which they bring and the reputational kudos associated with third party accreditation we will argue that they have also provided a 'paper shield' which generates a degree of false comfort for managers today. This shield gets in the way and distances us from those we need to work with – our staff – the human beings who may be affected adversely by their work, but also those who know what the solutions are.

Growing ranks of practitioners have added layers of complexity and tell us that we must manage ever decreasing levels of risk. We will show how learning from someone else's philosophy or methodology can be valuable, before arguing that it only *really works* if you decide how to make it work *in your own business*. It's about mindset over matter. We'll explore how to work out what good looks like and how to decide what is *just right* for your organization.

By the time we reach chapter four, you'll be clear on the issues that stand in the way of creating great safety leadership, so we'll look towards the future and help you to start building a different paradigm. You'll understand that some progress has already been made in breaking out of the cycle – the talk for some organizations is starting to feature 'health and safety leadership'. But leadership by whom and on what exactly? We'll show in this chapter that it's not about kids playing conkers and baskets of flowers falling on our heads, it's about identifying the real risks and managing them.

It's also about identifying those who may stand in the way of you creating the culture you want in your business and working with them in a different way so that you own the agenda, and they become an effective support team.

We'll explain why when it comes to matters of safety that it's really all about deciding for yourself how you want your business to be run and what sort of reputation you want to build for the business with your workforce and your wider stakeholders. It's about understanding and focusing on the real risks and being brave enough to say what you're not going to do because it's unimportant or bureaucratic – rather than blame it on some health and safety regulation that simply doesn't exist. Most of all, though, this chapter is about helping you to see leadership in health and safety as a strategy for success, not simply a means of reducing the risk of failure and accidents.

Finally, in chapter five, we will take you through the skills you need to make this new paradigm a reality. The good news is that it's not about having all of the answers – it's about knowing the right questions to ask.

We will walk you through a process of reflection and ask you to look deep inside yourself to find the answers to questions such as:

- Do I really understand what the risks are in this business?

- Am I confident that what is being reported to me truly represents the state of things?

- Would I know what to do if the worst were to happen?

Don't worry – even if the answer to these and the others questions we ask is '*I don't know*' then all is not lost by any means. We'll then move on to sharing questions that you can ask to others to get a unique insight into what's really going down. We'll explain why it's not all about hazard-spotting walkabouts and why getting out there and talking to people in a real and practical way is much more effective – and efficient. By asking what concerns them and how you can help them to create a safer workplace and by listening hard (but not pretending you have a magic wand – you can't do everything) you'll be able to identify and commit to doing the most important things first – once you really understand what they are. Now that's leadership!

At some point, of course, you will need a basic understanding of what the law requires of you and your colleagues – but that really isn't where to start. Start always with managing and leading the people, showing them you care, and you'll soon find that the rest will follow.

Ultimately we want to encourage you to decide how you want to lead your business and motivate the staff. You can decide how to meet the outcomes-based standards of health and safety that are required of your business.

Safety leadership really is about *minding your own business* because you care about the business and the people in it – and about sleeping soundly at night knowing you've done the right thing. Not doing it because someone else said you *had to do it.*

This book is about your leadership and how this will create just the right culture for immediate and sustained success for you and your business. We hope you enjoy both reading it and putting it into practice.

Dame Judith Hackitt & Andrew Sharman, January 2017

Long experience has taught me that the crux of my fortunes is whether I can radiate good will toward my audience. There is only one way to do it and that is to feel it. You can fool the eyes and minds of the audience, but you cannot fool their hearts.

Howard Thurston, Magician

CHAPTER 1

Exploring the Modern Myths of Health and Safety

No matter in which industry sector, country or region of the world we find ourselves, when it comes to matters of health and safety, myths abound. So let's start our journey by exploring this mythical world and develop an understanding of how it plays such a key – and often damaging – part in setting the scene for managing and leading health and safety in any business.

In recent years, both broadsheet and tabloid newspapers have heralded the state of the world of workplace safety. It seems to be a topic that not only grabs the headlines, but fuels a culture of fear within modern society. It's easy to laugh at the stories we see in the media, which typically begin with something like:

"Health and safety bans school sports day"

"Health and safety zealots ban bunting and Christmas lights"

"Health and safety stops hot drinks service"

We imagine that you have seen similar. These headlines may appear funny but the reality behind them is not. The headlines featured above are not examples written by us; each has appeared in the media – some more than once. And there are many more besides. All relate to real events which have taken place. What's interesting to us is that newspapers don't have to make up these headlines to grab readers' attention – they don't need to because too many people are actually generating the material for them already.

The school sports day story has appeared on several occasions in various different media channels. Whilst the headline is often the same, the details behind it vary from event to event. We know of one sports day that was cancelled because there had been a lot of rain in the preceding week and the grass was feared to be too slippery – so it could be argued that it was actually the rain – rather than health and safety – which stopped play. Another sports day was cancelled because it was feared that *'spectators'* (aka parents and families!) might want to take photos and it was impossible to meet the requirements of supposed *'safeguarding rules'*. Even where sports days are not totally written off, their content is heavily sanitised. The great British egg and spoon race fails to feature in many school events now, and where it clings on, the eggs have been replaced with solid plastic 'eggs' in order to *'reduce the risk of salmonella poisoning'*. Of course, safety killing school sports day is not a UK phenomenon. In America the three-legged race – where two kids are connected at the ankle and then run towards a finish line – was pulled from the program because of a rule that required all races are *'operated without risk of injury'*. In Switzerland, the sack race has also been 'banned by health and safety' for fears that children would take a tumble. We can both recall a time where actually falling over in these races was the part we all looked forward to and where the fun came from! In many countries parents are required to sign official disclaimer documents promising not to raise a claim against the school in the event of an accident – before their children can even take part. Perhaps you have your own observations on these 'stories', but the key question we want to pose here on the start of our health and safety journey is: why *cancel* these events rather than finding a solution that means the kids and their parents and friends don't have to miss out? Reschedule for another day, put up a sign asking people not to use cameras and try not to distract the kids. Really, just think pragmatically about what's planned and what might happen: it's not exactly rocket science!

Hanging out bunting to celebrate special occasions and putting up lights at Christmas-time brings out a different range of issues – these can range from a reluctance to offend some parts of the community by celebrating a festival they may not recognise or share; the chance of decorations being a distraction to drivers; their potential to attract crowds of people to see the spectacle (and thus, we imagine causing a risk of being trampled, crushed or rioted by the crowd); and in some cases we've even come across concerns that stringing lights or flags between lampposts might cause the lampposts to fall over and injure someone! It's not all about super-cautious behaviour either. Some people call on health and safety myths to justify behaviour which is anything but safe – Andrew has lost count of the number of taxi drivers who when challenged by him as to why they're not wearing a seat belt respond with *"for health and safety reasons."*[1] Is that *really* the reason?

You've likely heard of the huge class action suit taken against a global fast-food retailer following customers spilling coffee on their hands, the conclusion of which – beyond the millions in pay-outs to those 'injured' –was that each coffee cup is now labelled with the somewhat obvious *'Warning – contents may be hot'* sign. We've seen hot drinks being restricted to service in train restaurant carriages and consumers prohibited from taking the drinks back to their seats. Hot drinks are even banned in school lunch boxes – even if they're sealed in proper containers, and at mother and toddler groups too. In the latter case, surely it's just common sense to ask that hot drinks be kept well away from play areas rather than banning them outright? In the others, are these 'new rules' weakening our ability (and arguably our human right) to make informed choices for ourselves? Before we answer these questions, for now let's stick with our myths and legends. We promise to come back to the topic of common sense again over the next few chapters of this book.

We've lost count of the number of coffee shops who have refused to provide hot water to heat up a baby's bottle or jar of baby food. Time and time again the 'reason' given is 'health and safety'. But it clearly isn't – it is nothing more nor less than a cover-up phrase for the reality of *'we just can't be bothered'*, an employee's bad attitude, or poor attention to customer service.

So why do people use health and safety to cover up for the real reasons behind their decisions?

Quite simply because it's an easy get-out clause. If anyone offers the 'health and safety' argument when they make an over the top decision or refuse to provide decent customer service, they've absolved themselves of blame or responsibility and passed it on to someone or something else. It's so much easier to blame someone else than to own up to something. Especially if that finger of blame can be pointed at a non-descript group called *'Health and Safety'*. There's a strong chance the response from the person on the receiving end of this message will be a shrug of the shoulders and a resigned *"Oh, them again."*

Very little of this actually has anything to do with the real topic of this book – which is about managing and leading health and safety in *your* business. But it's important to understand what lies behind this strange but pervasive attitude to health and safety – and the impact that it has on all of us. When you go out to talk to your workforce to discuss the important health and safety issues that can actually cause real harm it's essential that you understand where the cynics among them could be coming from[2]. Because that is what this nonsense done in the name of health and safety has created – cynicism in very large measure, which makes the task of those of us who are trying to deal with real health and safety very much more difficult indeed.

And it's not just that this stuff deals with trivial risks where the consequences of anything really serious happening are almost non-existent. There is also an underlying bigger issue here which can best be described as *"don't blame me, blame them."* Or in other words, the replacement of personal responsibility with a blame culture which seeks to pass off responsibility onto someone – anyone – else. Understanding the impact of these myths and legends is fundamental to building the right culture in your organization and has to be addressed. So let's dig a bit deeper…

Responsibility – just whose line is it anyway?

When Judith started her first job as a graduate in the 1970s at one of the Europe's largest oil and petrochemical complexes, she passed through the security gates into the complex and noticed that a huge oil storage tank had been painted with a picture of a man pointing his finger at everyone who entered through the gate saying quite clearly *"You are responsible for safety on this site"*. Judith passed that sign every day for fifteen years and the message stuck with her – and everyone else that worked there. But her training in personal responsibility started way before then. You see, we both belong to that generation who, if they found themselves somewhere they probably shouldn't have been – like getting into trouble with teachers at school – they thought twice about telling parents because we'd just be even more likely to be asked to explain our bad behaviour all over again. Personal responsibility was a value instilled in both of us and in our peers at an early age. Being able to recognise when you have made a mistake and owning that mistake is an essential part of learning the lessons which we then carry with us for the rest of our lives.

So, what has changed? Where does this desire to pin it on someone else come from? In part at least it has been driven by easy access to 'compensation'. Let's be clear, we're not arguing against the need for anyone who has suffered real harm through absolutely no fault of their own and because of someone else's negligence or oversight to be able to seek recompense for their loss, damage or disability. But this is a question of balance. If I trip over in the street and cut my knee who is to blame? More than likely it's me, because I wasn't looking where I was going. In fact, today, there are countless people out there who are at risk of falling over in the street for precisely that reason – often because they are busy texting or tweeting – they expect everyone else to steer a path around them as they walk along engrossed in their phone or reading their tablet!

But let us consider what happens in some of these cases. The injured party goes home. They may have a very sore knee and so they put their feet up and watch TV. It won't be very long before the advertisement pops up on the TV – *"Have you been injured? You may be entitled to compensation…"* it continues with *"Call this number for free and we will make a claim on your behalf."* Listening carefully, our injured party's mind is now conjuring up all the things it could do with a cash windfall: paying off credit card debts; a present for their significant other; a cracking night out; or perhaps that dream holiday. The advert goes on: *"There's absolutely no cost to you, and if we don't win your case, you won't have anything to pay. It's even free to call us!"* At this point the hook is pretty much set, and the TV just needs to reel in the prize catch. Beaming from the screen we meet *'Kevin from London'* who *"won* £12,000 after an injury at work" and *'Carol from Scotland'* who's holding a giant cheque for the sum of £8,000.

It seems that our injured party has nothing to lose, so why not give it a shot? Perhaps there was a crack in the pavement that caused him to trip. No need to go back and check, someone else will do that and investigate – and it's free. Free to him that is, but the costs of course do get picked up elsewhere. As soon as the claim is made the charges begin. In the real world of work, those handling and processing such claims in commercial organizations (like our injured party's employer) and staff at the insurance companies see them as something of a nuisance. Costly to investigate properly, so it can be seen as much easier – and more cost effective – to settle quickly by just offering a payment and hoping it goes away. Certainly these small claims can appear cost effective to settle if you view each case in isolation and in the short term, but absolutely not when we consider the impact that this activity is having more broadly. If the claim is successful, our injured party will tell friends, and their reaction is likely to be *"I wonder if I could get some of that?"*. No matter where we are around the world, it's happening right now. The constant stream of *'no win-no fee'* advertisements on TV, in hospital waiting rooms, on buses, in taxis, and via unsolicited calls to our phones creates a climate which feeds the growth of this blame culture. *"Where's there's blame, there's a claim"* they tell us.

There are of course some who continue to argue that many developed nations don't have a compensation culture based on the number of claims which are made that simply don't succeed. But this attitude ignores two problems: one, the sheer volume of advertising which encourages us all to blame someone else, never ever mentioning our own personal responsibilities; and two, the time and cost incurred by business in defending those claims even if they are vexatious and there is no pay-out for the claim itself.

The first of these points is crucial, so let's get it on the table because it really is well and truly another myth – we cannot *always* blame someone else; first and foremost we need to consider what responsibility *we* need to take for our own actions. We acknowledge that this is easier said than done, of course, especially in a world where access to information and news is instant. As soon as any incident – large or small – is reported in the media, the pressure will be on to find out what went wrong and to find someone to blame. And we've seen this time and time again. Think back to any of the tragic events involving 'accidents' over the last few years. Finding someone to point the finger at and hold accountable is top priority. The captain of the cruise ship, the fat-cat CEO, the Chief Engineer who forgot to close the valve, the co-pilot – it's in our nature to single *someone* out. News coverage these days also tends to hinge on personal interest – what does this mean for me? Do I know anyone who was affected? Finding and taking the time to reflect on what really happened and what can be learned from any incident is increasingly difficult in an age of instant news and short attention spans. And taking responsibility is the hard choice if you know someone else is going to point the finger of blame at <u>you</u>.

So all of this leads us to other mythical quests. Namely the search for 'absolute safety' and for a guarantee that these things *"will never happen again."* How many times have you read, said or heard the following question: *"Is it safe?"*? As organizations strive to improve workplace safety, more and more managers and leaders ask the question as if it is some kind of demonstration of their personal commitment or a panacea for convincing workers and facilitating their engagement. It's not. Because <u>safety is not an absolute</u>. In his practical guide to safety culture, *From Accidents to Zero*, Andrew wrote about the growing fascination with eliminating all risk and attaining zero accidents. He argues that the quest for absolute safety is founded upon the concept of binary opposition, where things are explained using two mutually opposing terms. Simply put, if it's not one thing, it must be the other. So, with regard to safety, things are either 'safe' or 'unsafe'. Whilst we'd very much like to think we've moved beyond those days of things being either being black or white, in our recent experience it doesn't appear that things have progressed that much – and in fact, we fear a regression is in play.

Safety – at the most fundamental level – is a matter of judgment and balance. It involves complex issues of understanding the distinction between hazard and risk, assessing risk tolerance, evaluating risk perception, comparative assessment of risks versus other options, value judgements on the benefits to be gained versus the level of risk involved and who is perceived to be in control of imposing the risk.

Much has been written on this topic by others, but it is worthwhile to highlight here a couple of examples of when and why the *"Is it safe?"* question is posed:

"Is it safe to let children play outdoors?"

Some of the hazards of playing outdoors are obvious and spring instantly to mind – traffic on the street; trees to fall from; water to fall in; access to building sites; dangerous dogs; predatory strangers – we can quickly build a list. But let's first of all acknowledge that playing or passing time *indoors* also means we encounter hazards – matches or the means to start a fire; electrical equipment; household chemicals which may be poisonous; hot kettles and irons; staircases; access to unsuitable material on TV – and increasingly for every child, via the internet. So in an attempt to move beyond a binary choice answer, perhaps the question should be *"Which is safer?"* But this is also difficult to answer because we would be trying to compare different hazards and consequences, wouldn't we? The danger of falling from a tree is easy to imagine and it's immediate; but on the other hand the potential for a lifetime of inactivity to be inculcated by hours spent in front of a TV or computer screen is diffuse. Our perception is distorted in part by what we read and see in the media – every child abducted makes headlines and our instinct is to assume it is by a stranger. Each time the headline appears, parents reinforce the family rules with their children and restrict their opportunities to play outside, or go to the park on their own. Yet the reality is that the *incidence* of child abduction is no greater today than in the past – it's the news coverage that's much greater. Bear in mind too that a significant proportion of these cases also turn out to be attributable to someone who is known to the child and the family, not to a stranger. But for most parents the biggest fear that gets in the way of letting children play outdoors remains this notion of 'stranger danger'. And it is not difficult to see how we opt for the protective option.

But what about the benefits of exposure to hazard and risk? Spending one's childhood being closely supervised and wrapped in cotton wool – avoiding all hazards indoors or out – will certainly ensure no harm – at least for the time being – but what of the longer term? If children don't experience excitement and fear as part of play activity how will they be equipped to deal with the world around them as they grow up? We believe that education and parenting needs to be about helping our children to recognise hazards and learning how to handle them as and when we encounter them, not avoiding them altogether. We need to recognise that we cannot create a risk-free environment for our children and that if we try to, they will be only exposed to a different set of risks later – which they may well be unaware of and fully ill-equipped to deal with.

"Is it safe to travel by a particular means or to a specific place?"

In the aftermath of any transport incident involving multiple fatalities – such as a train or aeroplane crash – this question is likely to be raised. It's a natural response to a tragic event, isn't it? Yet in fact, the most hazardous means of transport which any of us will ever use is well-known to us and usually one we utilise frequently – driving a car or motorcycle, or riding a bicycle. The statistics clearly show that the number of fatalities on our roads exceed those in plane and train related incidents *combined*. But here is where our risk tolerance and risk perception come into play. When we drive, we consider ourselves to be 'in control'. Over the last few years we've been asking groups and individuals whether they feel they are a good driver. Of course everyone said yes (including us!). No-one we know thinks they are not a good driver. This self-confidence in our driving ability leads people to believe that they will not become one of the statistics of road traffic accidents. When we delved further into the perceptions of drivers, many supported their assertions of being a good driver with a statement outlining that they had not suffered any road accidents – some, over very long periods of time. By comparison, control of the plane or train is down to others – in these instances we are passengers and clearly we are not 'in control'. So driving feels safer than it actually is, and travelling by other means feels less safe because others are making decisions for us.

Familiarity also impacts upon what we perceive as being safe. Travelling to parts of the world which we are not familiar with may cause us to think long and hard about whether it is safe, but do we give the same consideration to travelling to parts of our own country where there may be similar hazards awaiting the unwary or adventurous traveller? As international travel becomes more accessible, our familiarity grows. And so too does our confidence. In recent times we have seen atrocities committed in places where many, many of us have felt 'in control', 'safe', and free from such previously unimaginable risks. We don't need to list the cities. The fact is, the world is getting smaller. But is it also getting more dangerous? Or are our brains playing tricks on us to make us believe it is so? We propose that it's the latter.

Few people would argue with the view that when any one of us goes out to work every day, we have the right to expect to come home again unharmed by the work that we've done. Most of the time we take it for granted that this will be the case – unless or until something happens to shake us out of that comfort zone (just like how our confidence in air travel is rocked by a plane crash). Just like when we travel by plane, at work people place a great deal of faith in others to look out for them and ensure that when they interact with the services they provide that they will not be put at risk.

Just think of our world today. There is plenty of evidence we are being encouraged to operate with a mind set on autopilot. When you get up in the morning, one push of a button and you receive your morning coffee just the way you like it: the correct size, taste, temperature – even flavour and milk combinations – are all pre-set just for you. If you hop into your car, and forget to fasten your seatbelt an alarm will remind you to put it on. When the skies darken the car's headlights turn themselves on. If it starts to rain the windscreen wipers are activated. Messages on your dashboard advise when the best time to select the next gear is, in order to maximise fuel efficiency. Joining the highway, a flick of a switch selects a speed to control your cruising speed and you can take your foot off the gas. If you're fortunate (or wealthy) your vehicle may even sense you drifting out of your lane or getting too close to the vehicle in front and correct your position automatically. If you take a wrong turn or miss your exit, the GPS system will not only tell you, but also plan a new route and advise you of your revised arrival time in a softly-spoken voice of your choosing. And if, by the time you arrive at work, all this technology has caused your mind to wander, and you get too close to a colleague's car as you manoeuvre your way into your space, the proximity switches will beep to let you know. Before unbuckling, a final update from the car: the vehicle monitoring system will warn you of any faults that need to be looked at and remind you when the next service is due.

The list of safety features on cars today is endless when we compare them with even a few years ago and driving has – as you might expect – become much safer as a result. Despite this immense technological progress the most important safety feature of every car may not be as up to date as those others we've described here. That safety feature is you. The driver of the car, behind the wheel – and, of course, what is going on inside your head.

Think about what happens if you are driving and you come across a road traffic accident. Everyone we've spoken to says the same thing – they take a look at what has occurred (whether this is part of a dynamic risk assessment, an instinctive desire for the macabre, or a vested interest in the robustness of modern vehicle design, we cannot confirm) and when they have passed the crash and the road is clear again they drive much more cautiously – for a while – because they've been reminded that driving is not quite as safe as they thought. Some people even suggest that it's a good thing for new young drivers to be involved in some minor road traffic accident early in their driving career as a direct experiential way of learning that they're not invincible. It may work for those it happens to but we would certainly not advocate this as a good idea! There are other ways for young drivers to learn and the same is true in workplaces – you don't have to wait for someone to get hurt before people take safety seriously. We also need to consider the issues of risk perception, so let's explore some of the examples we've introduced. Our attitude to driving versus flying or taking the train is a good place to begin. Travelling by train or plane are statistically demonstrably safer than driving but many of us fear flying because of the fact that someone else is in control – rather than us. Train and plane crashes are still, fortunately, relatively rare but when one occurs it *always* make the news headlines – so when they do happen we hear about it: we hear how many people died; the search for survivors; we see the distress of their families waiting for news. We take it all in and somewhere in our brains we register that it could have been us. This could happen to us. We feel a sense of outrage because the victims were innocent – they could have done nothing to avoid the tragedy, they were just there. But perhaps *others* could have done something to avoid this terrible event.

Compare this to road traffic accidents. Unless there are multiple fatalities most of us will not even get to hear about the fatal and serious incidents that happen on the roads around us every single day. If we do happen to hear about an incident, more often than not it is because our own journey is disrupted by the delays to traffic which follow from road closures and vehicle recoveries. We've already talked about the short term effect which is likely to occur to our own driving habits if we pass the scene of an incident, but for the most part we all get behind the wheel confident in the knowledge that we are all 'good drivers' and therefore 'it won't happen to us'. We have managed to rationalise the risks associated with driving because of the benefits it brings – the convenience, the flexibility, the ability it gives us to go where we want when we want and also because of our personal experience. We drive more frequently than we take other forms of transport and every time we complete a successful incident-free trip it reinforces our view that driving is 'safe'. Our perception of the risks of driving is skewed compared to other safer forms of transport. This mental skewing is an important issue to be aware of because similar skewing of risks occurs in the workplace – as we will discuss later.

So now we've set some context, let's start exploring why health and safety is perceived as 'difficult' in so many workplaces. This chapter opened by looking at some of the modern myths at play in the wider context of the world around us because it's important to recognise that it is *all of our experiences* that shape our attitudes to risk – and to health and safety, as employers and as employees. It's clear that in the world of health and safety myths do abound. Some of these myths are familiar – perhaps like those we shared at the outset of this section – and some are just plain ridiculous. But it goes much deeper than that. The quest for absolute safety reflects a growing level of risk aversion everywhere we look, especially if deciding to take a risk involves owning up to personal responsibility and accountability if things go wrong.

We've already agreed that everyone who goes to work has a right to expect to go home at the end of every day unharmed by the work that they've done. But whose responsibility is it to ensure that they actually do? The answer, of course is that it is a shared responsibility between employer and employee. In many countries this is enshrined in law. In the United Kingdom, the Health and Safety at Work Act of 1974 states that there is a duty on the employer to manage the risks created in the business, but there is also a legal duty placed on every employee to act in such a way that they do not create risk for themselves or their colleagues. In the United States the Occupational Safety & Health Act, which came into law in 1971, sets out to assure safety and healthy working conditions for those at work. In Australia and New Zealand there has been significant work in recent years to harmonise an approach to providing workers with protection from health and safety risks in the workplace. And in South Africa, Canada, parts of Asia and across Europe, and in many other countries in between, right around the globe, there are equivalent laws. Each set out similar *shared* responsibilities.

It is easy to understand why so much emphasis is placed on the former – the duty of the employer. The person who owns or runs the business creates a level of risk by the nature of the business they are in. It may be a high hazard industry – such as oil & gas or chemical processing, or mining, quarrying or industrial manufacturing – where a comprehensive risk management system will need to be in place – or it simply may be a low hazard business such as services provided in an office environment where the risks are fairly obvious to everyone and significantly less expertise will be required to manage those risks. The law is equally clear and it applies to high and low risk environments. There is no legal intent to stop anyone from doing what they are in business to do – as long as the risks are identified and managed as far as is reasonable and practicable. There is no requirement under any law to eliminate risk. Let's repeat that to be absolutely clear – there is no requirement to *eliminate* risk – that simply would be neither reasonable nor practicable. Just as with the impossible quest for absolute safety, no environment – at work or at home – can be made risk free. But what we can do is what is reasonable and that is to think about and identify the risks, to consider what we can do practically to reduce them and to also consider what we will need to be prepared to do if something goes wrong.

So now let's move forward and consider perspectives on this first step in managing safety – namely that of risk assessment – both inside and outside the workplace.

Risk assessments – paper exercise or state of mind?

"How many risk assessments have you completed?"

A common enough question to ask at work but we want to continue to explore the disconnect between life inside and outside of the workplace a bit more. Taken in the broader context – in the world outside of the workplace, the only smart answers can be – *"No idea"* or *"I've lost count"*. But when we talk about risk assessment in the workplace what immediately springs to many minds is a bureaucratic process that gets in the way of getting the job done.

Here's the problem. Risk assessment in the workplace has become a pedantic paper-driven exercise. It's no longer simply a means of recording the important things you've thought about and taken action on but for many has become paperwork for its own sake. When we ask leaders why they do this, almost without exception every single one declares that they *"need to be able to prove"* what they are doing *"just in case something bad happens."*

Over in the world outside of work, those super-cautious parents we talked about earlier have done their risk assessments too – and concluded that the world is such a dangerous place that their child must be protected from it at all costs. Their risk assessments are flawed, however, as they have a hugely distorted perception of the risks and a highly emotional view of the potential consequences. Whilst not great, at least their problem is certainly not one of paperwork and bureaucracy.

The fact is that we are all doing risks assessments all of the time. We don't call them that and we may not even recognise when we are doing them. But we are. For most of us, here in the real world, our life experiences have shaped our thinking about risk and as a result most times our 'autopilot' switches on and our brain assesses the risk in the things we do without us even thinking consciously about it.

Here's an example: Before we leave the house to go to work we do many risk assessments:

- *Do I need a coat or an umbrella?*

- *What are the chances of rain?*

- *Will it turn cold later?*

- *Can I afford to take the time to do some laundry or empty the dishwasher and still catch my train?*

- *If I do these chores, will I need to drive faster to the station and possibly break the speed limit?*

- *What if there's a hold up en-route to work?*

- *If I put myself under time pressure what else could happen?*

- *Is it really worth it?*

The above is a real-life risk assessment. It's often the early morning routine for both of us. Is it just us, because we're fanatical about health and safety? We don't think we're alone in going through these thought processes (But please tell us if we are!) What we've described here is just one tiny example of the way we all consider and weigh up risks, benefits and consequences – often against other risks, benefits and consequences – all of the time. It's how we live our lives and how we survive.

We've already recognised that there's a strong element of personal bias that creeps into some of these assessments that we all carry out, often subconsciously. So let's now look deeper.

We all have different ways of managing the risks. The really organised ones among us will do a bit of pre-planning to allow more time – setting the alarm clock five minutes earlier, or delegating – leaving a note to ask the kids to empty the dishwasher. Some will decide to leave the tasks to avoid the pressure of rushing for the train. Others will do the chores anyway and hope they can still catch the train – that will depend on their *risk appetite*. The coat and umbrella decision may depend on information you've received from experts – for example the weather forecast on television (which perfectly provides you with 'someone else to blame' if you get wet or cold having taken their advice) or it may be driven by the consequences – sitting in an important meeting with wet hair and wet clothes is a much more serious consequence and therefore a bigger risk to take than if this is a day to be spent in the office with no meetings or if you routinely change into different work clothes when you arrive at work.

We will talk much more about the need to think through the consequences later, because of course, it's not really risk assessment that matters – it's the risk *management* that counts. The vitally important point to note here is the ubiquity of assessing risks. We are literally all doing it, all of the time. We may not always get it right in which case hopefully we learn from our mistakes and become wiser for next time, but it is a fundamental life skill, developed from our times living in caves and chasing / being chased by a T-Rex (depending on your risk appetite!) – without it we simply wouldn't survive.

So how can we avoid turning a natural process which we are all so familiar with into a bureaucratic process which switches everyone off when we apply it in the workplace?

Well, we think that before you can manage risks you need to know what they are and which are the ones that can cause real harm – that's the *proper* purpose of the risk assessment. In the UK, the Health & Safety

Executive's[3] guidance states very clearly that:

"A risk assessment is not about creating huge amounts of paperwork, but rather about identifying sensible measures to control the risks."

The guidance continues:

"You do not need to take action if it would be grossly disproportionate to the level of risk."

And when it comes to paperwork the guidance says:

"Make a record of your findings… (they) should be simple and focused on controls"

and:

"Any paperwork you do produce should help you to communicate... this does not need to be a big exercise – just note down the main points about the significant risks and what you concluded."

There you have it: in just 86 words you now know everything you need to know about risk assessment. But given that this is a practical book we think that we can go further and summarise all of that as:

"Do what makes sense and don't go over the top."

Remember those myths and legends we mentioned earlier? These have helped to turn workplace risk assessment into an activity so challenging and complex that only 'experts' are perceived to be able to complete the task effectively. Here's three further examples, all taken from our contact with real organizations (perhaps just like yours).

Myth 1: Comprehensive proformas which cover every possible risk in every possible scenario are designed by experts to be helpful to the uninitiated and unfamiliar.

No doubt created with the best of intentions, but it turns out they're not very helpful and can be both confusing and tedious. They become a box-ticking exercise full of irrelevant questions which don't apply to the situation being considered and where the real risks may get lost or may not even have been considered, especially if the wrong proforma has been used.

Here's a quick example: Judith's daughter studied Marine Biology at University. In her final year she had to undertake a research project and was able to choose from a list of options provided by the University. Somewhat surprisingly given her love of diving, she chose to do desk-based literature research on her chosen subject rather than undertaking field studies – as did many of her classmates. But her University still sent her a twelve page risk assessment form to complete before she could get started on her project. She called her mother: *"Do I really have to fill in all of this nonsense when all I'm going to do is sit at my computer? I've been doing that for the last three and a half years and I'm not doing anything different on this project!"* If the research project had involved lots of practical work, possible expeditions out to sea or underwater, conducting a risk assessment would be a very good idea. But why does an educational establishment take this sort of blanket approach, handing out the same long proformas to everyone? A good risk assessment in this case would have asked some sensible questions, perhaps like:

- What are you proposing to do for your project?

- Does this involve any new activities which you have not done before?

- What could go wrong during your project?

- What harm could be caused: – To you? – To others?

- What can you do to minimise those risks?

- Do you need any help or advice from others to manage the risks? If so discuss them with your tutor

Judith's daughter didn't complete the twelve page questionnaire (rightfully, we think). After discussion with her mum, she simply wrote on the form that there were no new risks to consider so a risk assessment for this project was unnecessary. But how many of her classmates just sighed and dogmatically filled in the form? We imagine that this exercise left them with a very bad taste for what risk assessment is all about – on what would for many have been, their first encounter.

Myth 2: Risk assessments must be done – and written down – for everything, every time a job is done

The guidance in the UK (and in most other developed nations around the world) is clear: it talks about – *"main points"* and *"significant risks"*. Under British law if you employ fewer than five employees you don't even have to write anything down. The main purpose of writing the material down is to explain to others what the risks are and what has been done or needs to be done to manage them. Clearly if you employ larger groups and teams of people, having your findings written down makes them easier to communicate.

Employers need to do risk assessments for what their employees will do but these can cover a collection of similar tasks. Examples where one risk assessment could cover many activities could include: 'warehouse operations' – for routine and repetitive tasks, as long as the assessment takes account of the hazards and risks in that particular workplace; particular requirements for certain workers – new and inexperienced people, those with disability or physical impairment, pregnant workers, lone workers and so on. Given that a key purpose of the assessment is to communicate the risks to those who will do the work, keeping the language simple and straightforward makes a lot of sense – there's no requirement to use technical jargon, complex abbreviations or anything else, just use words and phrases that are in common use. Risk assessments don't need to be done repeatedly – all that is needed is for them to be reviewed from time to time to check whether anything has changed and to update them as required.

One of the common myths we've encountered with risk assessments is in cases of providing work experience for students. Work experience is an important part of educating young people and preparing them for the world of work. One of the barriers to setting up work experience often cited by would-be employers (and educators – as we illustrated in the story above) is the need to carry out extensive risk assessments – but it really is a myth. If you've taken the approach of considering the needs of the young and inexperienced already as part of your risk assessment process the job is already done. If you haven't considered them then you just need to revisit your existing risk assessments and update them – but only on the first occasion that you employ someone on work experience. Someone will of course need to make sure that the young person understands the risks involved in the work they do – but that is far better covered as part of their induction training. Remember that our task here is to communicate the risks and how to stay safe around them – simply handing them or their teacher a copy of the risk assessment doesn't really do the job for anyone.

Myth 3: Risk assessments must be stand-alone documents, kept in a comprehensive file of their own.

The purpose of conducting a risk assessment is to decide what action needs to be taken to manage the risk – and then taking those steps. The format of risk assessments can vary enormously depending on the organization and the situation. In manufacturing industries, standard operating procedures are commonplace. Good operating procedures will not only describe how to do the job when all is well but will cover what to do when the unexpected or unusual happens – and the risk assessment information can be incorporated within the procedures.

The Health Care sector routinely produce 'Care Plans' which describe how a vulnerable patient is to be cared for. It is clear that a proper care plan needs to consider what hazards and vulnerabilities there are for that individual (risk of choking, ability to walk unaided and so on) and record them in the plan. It seems obvious to us then that this means the risk assessment has been done as an integral part of developing the care plan. There is no need to do a risk assessment as a separate exercise as long as the risks have been considered as they should be – as an integral part of caring for the patient.

For a teacher, about to take a group of children out of the classroom on a geography trip to a local woodland, the best place to record the risk assessment may be on a board or chart in the classroom. The risk assessment can be part of the preparatory lesson, involving the children in thinking about what hazards they might encounter on their visit and what they need to do to keep safe. Rather than keeping a paper risk assessment for the files, a photo of what was written on the chart could be taken for future reference.

So what we've tried to do here is show a few ways in which risk assessment can be incorporated into the tasks in a variety of workplaces by exploring the heavy myths that sit around safety. Our list isn't comprehensive and the intention is to prompt you to think about how you could make risk assessment more integrated in your workplace. We hope it's a helpful start for you.

Laugh and the whole world laughs with you. But does it really?

It's easy to laugh at those headlines at the start of this chapter, isn't it? The well-informed amongst our readers may also have laughed at these myths about risk assessments. You may even be thinking that perhaps we've made them up or embellished them for effect. During the research for this book we spoke with many organizations and individuals, including business leaders and safety professionals. Here's a thought shared by one of them:

"I've been working for some 48 years now in a range of roles, the past ten or so years in the field of health and safety. I often find it frustrating that even within our own organization, colleagues make silly comments like "Have you done a risk assessment for making that coffee?" or "Have you done a manual handling assessment for moving that chair?" These comments are intended as humorous banter but often they get a swift and unrepeatable response from me – with a smile, of course. I like to think, and hopefully in my job role, I haven't contributed to their perceptions around health and safety because I really do try to focus on issues where serious harm could arise and really am not too interested in paper cuts and spilling coffee." MB, Safety Advisor, UK

MB is not alone. Over the last decade we've both been on the receiving end of similar comments – more than we can count, or recall here in this book. So what? Well, each of the alternative solutions outlined for the headlines at the start of this chapter and in our simple ways of incorporating risk assessment into everyone's role demonstrate that risk assessments can and should be done in ways that work for a particular organization. The job of the manager and leader in any organization – whether university, factory, warehouse, hospital or school – is to ensure that risk assessments are *suitable and sufficient* – a phrase featured in many contemporary health and safety regulations. To be suitable and sufficient the assessment process must work for your employees and others who may be exposed to risk – they need to be able to understand the risks which relate to the task and how to do the job safely by doing as they have been trained to do, not deviating from procedures, wearing the right gear for the job and so on. That means the information has to be accessible and available at the time and place where the activity takes place and can be used there and then – not gathering dust on a shelf in the safety manager's office. They have to be accessible and they have to make sense to the person who needs to read them.

Beyond the burdens of bureaucracy

We've already explored some of the obstacles and the myths that get in the way of real safety in the workplace. Yet is there more to it than that? We've just shared some examples which reveal that much of what is called 'health and safety' is actually more about providing paperwork as evidence in the event that a claim is made. Though could we be overcomplicating things and creating burdens for ourselves by over interpreting what is required? We think someone is.

We've already started to expose some of the ways in which legal requirements get over-interpreted when it comes to risk assessment.

Now we want to explore some of the other ways in which workplaces lose some of their perspective on health and safety by looking at the role of communication, systems and balance.

Don't say it if you don't mean it!

Lots of business leaders claim that health and safety is their 'Number 1 priority' but do they really mean it? The only organizations for which health and safety can possibly be the number one priority are those whose businesses actually *are* health and safety – it's what they are in business to do. So, for example, it could be described as the number one priority of the *Health & Safety Executive* – which exists to prevent death, injury and ill health in Great Britain's workplaces. But it is interesting that even the regulator doesn't choose to make such a statement about its own role. The latest strategy for the HSE describes its strategic priorities in terms of awareness raising in Small and Medium-sized Enterprises; raising the profile of work-related health issues; and holding poor performers to account. The difference of course is that progress in achieving these more specific priorities can be measured. Managers in business – as those in the regulator – know how important measurement is and about the need to be specific.

Senior business leaders would be unlikely to say that *"Good financial accounting is our number one priority"* wouldn't they? Conducting the business with integrity, obeying the requirements of the law and having good financial risk management is part of how the leadership team decides it wants to operate – because it wants to runs its business well and stay within the law. This is about *how* the particular business will be run, not the *purpose* of the business. Good financial management may well be a priority if the company was trying to retrieve itself from a situation where it had been found lacking in an audit. Similarly, health and safety may be a company's number one priority if they have a very poor track record and their business is suffering as a result of it – either financially, with regard to reputation, or as a result of regulatory enforcement. But it will be their number one priority <u>until</u> the underlying problems are fixed. Then it reverts to becoming part of how the business is run.

Just like good financial management, we think that good health and safety should be a <u>core value</u>. It needs to be how the leaders of the business decide they want their organization to operate – because they care about how they do business as well as being successful at the particular business they are in.

The desire for certainty

It's a normal human trait to want to be assured that all is well. We all love stability and control. In fact, it's what the role of management is all about in many ways – ensuring that people know what to do and how to do it, thinking about what could go wrong and how those eventualities can be covered, seeking assurance that we are doing better than our competitors. We choose to put systems in place to create greater assurance, build confidence and gain control. Management systems can often provide a very good framework, especially in large and complex organizations with multiple locations and/or many employees. Standardising the way things are done and ensuring that everyone adopts the right approach is key to reliability, efficiency and good order. International standards have become immensely popular over the last 30 years or so. Perhaps your business uses a standardised system to manage quality or ensure that your environmental impact is minimised. Or maybe you've even installed a system to help you manage safety. Perhaps you have achieved third party accreditation of your systems which you display proudly on letterheads and websites.

But when it comes to management systems, there's a hidden trap. It's what Andrew calls being 'system obsessed'. We need to beware of creating a reliance on systems that gives a false sense of security. It is not uncommon for a manager to ask whether or not the business is *'in compliance'* with the system. The expert may pull down several folders from that dusty shelf, leaf through the pages and then proudly extract an audit document or checklist that concludes that they are indeed in compliance. The manager walks away feeling confident, the expert feeling proud. And the merry-go-round of tick-sheets, audits, checks and questions continues to revolve. But the nature of any business or enterprise is dynamic. Audits and checklist provide merely a snapshot in time. Systems are based on what is foreseeable – describing what should happen, anticipating what might occur in terms of unusual, but foreseeable, events and how to handle these. To some degree, management systems are created to deliver conformity but at the same time, they must not inhibit the ability of <u>people</u> to think for themselves. The danger manifests itself most obviously when the system becomes a checklist – as long as everything on the list is ok, everything is ok – and the humans switch to autopilot mode. *Very* not ok.

Managing health and safety *can* be systematised, but not to the extent that people stop thinking, or worse still become complacent that everything is in control and nothing can go wrong. Whilst we can, and should, achieve a level of assurance that systems are in place to deal with most events – and certainly those that can be anticipated – we also need to ensure that there remains within the organization a level of alertness to new risks and new events that arise and which may not be covered, even by the very best of systems. The best assurance comes from having people in the workforce who are trained to think and act appropriately for themselves.

Avoiding over-reaction and getting the balance *just right*

Once upon a time, there was a little girl with long, flowing blonde hair. Whilst walking in the forest one day she came across a pretty little house. On entering she found a table set for breakfast with three bowls of porridge. We're sure you know the classic fairytale of *Goldilocks and the 3 Bears*. You'll remember that as she tastes each bowl of porridge our heroine finds the first one 'too hot', the second 'too cold', but the third bowl is *'just right'*. The story continues with similar results for the chairs in the living room, and for the mattresses on the beds too. Carefully stepping over the debate about the dubious practice of breaking-and-entering (and especially the inherent dangers of doing this in a house inhabited by three grizzly bears!) we see this story as having synergy with managing workplace health and safety. The aim is to get things *'just right'*. Not too hot, not too cold. *Just right*. Now hold that thought – we'll ask you to return to it very shortly.

The problems associated with doing too little on workplace safety should be obvious. Organizations where little or no attention is paid to health and safety, for whatever reason, have no real and genuine belief that everyone should go home from work every day unharmed. In some, that may be because they choose to chance their luck, or perhaps because they've never yet experienced a serious event, or they don't actually share that core value we have already talked about. They are prepared to take a chance – often with someone else's health and wellbeing, but also occasionally with their own safety. In many such cases that we've come across it would be hard to imagine that risks were taken due to lack of knowledge or appreciation – at best, perhaps people assumed that their luck would hold. Of course, this book is not aimed at those people who regard health and safety as a game of chance.

But there are also organizations where too little is done because it all feels too difficult and too complicated. If this sounds familiar, please keep reading. We do want to help these businesses – by removing the complexity, by creating the freedom to do health and safety in a way that works for you and for your organization and which delivers not only good health and safety performance but also shows real tangible benefits in other ways – in productivity, workforce engagement and profits.

We also want to help leaders in organizations which are doing *too much*. Yes, we *do* think that it is possible to do too much in health and safety. We know companies where health and safety has somehow gone over the top. Where minor events are treated as major incidents, where the ability to exercise judgement and proportionality has been eroded or lost, and where health and safety really is getting in the way of doing the job efficiently and effectively.

That's why we talk about this being a balancing act and needing to get things, just like Goldilocks, *'just right'*.

Some readers may find the notion that we can do 'too much' health and safety quite difficult. We empathise with these readers, but we'll strive to convince you of our point of view by the time you get to the end of this book. We've already talked about the desire to create certainty and over-assurance – by trying to eliminate all risks – which, we hope you'll agree is just not possible. But let's look at three clear examples of how this frequently manifests itself in rules and behaviours – although often in disguise:

1 Blanket rules are created which are applied to everyone regardless of the situation and therefore the risk. Mandatory personal protective equipment <u>at all times</u> is an example. At a huge warehousing facility just off a main French *autoroute* the signs are everywhere. This global

freight and distribution company prides itself on its 'safety first' approach. On a recent visit Andrew was surprised to see the receptionist who welcomed him onto site get up from her desk and walk past him moments later wearing a pair of mid-ankle industrial steel toe-capped boots – on a designated pedestrian walkway with a robust steel barrier running along its perimeter, at least fifty metres from the nearest stock on a racking bay – *très chic!* – but also quite unnecessary.

2 An organizational culture where every incident – irrespective of outcome or potential outcome – must be investigated by a team of people and recommendations must always be made. In a major Fast Moving Consumer Goods company we visited, we learned of 'incidents' including an event where some coffee was spilled on a desk which necessitated the completion of a Near Miss report and a full investigation by the company safety manager and the department head. As a result of their findings, all hot drinks are no longer allowed at workstations and must now only be drunk in designated areas at the site canteen facilities. Come on! *Really?*

3 Soaring high above Capetown's Central Business District a new corporate head office looms large. The construction firm building the iconic commercial palace takes safety very seriously. Mandatory Personal Protective Equipment includes high-visibility vests, steel toe-cap boots, and a hard hat. On the roof terrace, like on the internal floors of the building employees must wear their head protection. Though there is nothing overhead except a bright blue South African sky and 38 degrees Celsius heat. When the site management departs the top floor what do you think the workers do? Yes, of course, remove their hats. But only until one of them gets fired, and then they all go back to sweltering under their plastic lids.

Examples like these demonstrate a serious lack of both proportionality and prioritisation. Some will argue that this somewhat totalitarian approach helps to create a 'real safety culture'. We have serious doubts. Time spent investigating trivial incidents can be time wasted. Employees will almost certainly question this lack of proportionality – among themselves even if not overtly – especially if they see attention being paid to such minor concerns whilst issues which are of much greater concern to them are not being tackled by management. Talking to members of such workforces about productivity improvement may also be challenging when they can point to obvious examples of time wasted and taken away from the real work.

When rules become restrictive and/or disproportionate, they create a response in those on the receiving end. Cynicism – as we just suggested – is one. A temptation to break the rules – especially where the worker believes that the rules don't make sense to them – is another. Just as we highlighted at the start of this chapter, the impact of this extends beyond the specific rule itself. Just as media stories about nonsensical bans in the name of health and safety create cynicism within society at large, rules imposed by you as the leader which feel disproportionate or irrelevant are likely to be counter-productive – leading to further scepticism rather than creating a healthy and positive culture and making it harder for you to lead them with a *just right* approach

So as we conclude this first chapter, we hope that you are starting to see that bringing some of that common sense which we use in our everyday lives into the workplace is not just possible but it is, in fact, desirable. We feel sure that not every reader will be at this point with us just yet, and some will no doubt be thinking *'If only it were that simple'*. Our task over the next few chapters is to explain that it is indeed that simple. It's about you deciding *for yourself* what kind of safety culture you want to create – it really is about *minding your own business*!

Having reached the end of this first chapter, now here's a few questions we'd encourage you to reflect on:

1 When you come across health and safety nonsense stories and myths in the newspaper, on the radio or on television how do you typically react?

2 Do you recognise the extent to which we all assess and manage risks as part of living our everyday lives?

3 Do you know how risk assessment is done in your organization?
 – Who does it?
 – Why?
 – What is the purpose of risk assessment in your workplace?
 – How could you integrate risk assessment into tasks and procedures in your workplace?

4 Is your safety management system *comprehensive but bureaucratic* or *practical, well understood and well-used*? Why do you think this is?

5 Where is your organization on the *'Goldilocks Scale'*? Too much health and safety? Too little? Or *'just right'*?

By the way, just one other myth we need to bust here: it's ok – at this stage – to answer *'I don't know'* to any of these questions above. We all need to understand what we don't know: it's the key to learning – and to leading well.

Footnotes

1 Typically the drivers offer that they fear being strangled by hooligan passengers, or that they *"need to be able to get out quickly to open doors"*. Interestingly, when asked to put the belt on or lose their fare, every driver without fail buckles up.

2 The over-the-top culture of fear we're describing here we think is one of the key factors that generate negative stigma around health and safety, but it's not the only one. We'll offer some other ideas as we continue our discussion.

3 The Health & Safety Executive is the regulator of health and safety law in Great Britain.

Don't let the noise of others' opinions drown out your own inner voice. Most important, have the courage to follow your heart and intuition.

Steve Jobs, Entrepreneur & Co-Founder of Apple

CHAPTER 2
But What If...?

In the previous chapter we explored some of the ways in which mythology and bureaucracy have been built up around the subject of health and safety. We could continue in that vein for much longer – but to what end? Instead, we hope that by now you will recognize some of the ways in which the subject has become distorted. Perhaps you are even starting to come up with examples of your own that you've come across. We will return later in this book to some of the obstacles we've talked about, but when we do, it will be to consider how we can remove those obstacles and tackle the whole subject in a more positive mindset, with you – the leader – in control; influencing and leading how things are done in your business. But for that to happen we have to get to a place where you feel confident to do this – especially when faced with 'experts' who will tell you that there are rules and requirements which you must follow – even when this isn't true.

In a world where we have more freedom and choice than ever before, and in an age where independence and opinion are the currencies of modern life, why is it that we seem to want to defer to a 'do as you're told' mindset when it comes to health and safety? What is it that we are afraid of? Why do so many leaders fear to manage health and safety with the positivity and confidence in which they manage others aspects of the business? In this chapter we'll explore why we have become so risk averse. Is it because society – with more than a little help from the media – has brought about a particular view of health and safety? And what really lies behind those very many ridiculous stories of innocuous activities banned in the name of health and safety?

Over the next few pages we'll explore why many leaders have handed over health and safety to a team of so called 'experts' rather than owning it and managing it themselves as business leaders. Is it because they have been told that it's so complex they can't possibly understand it, let alone do it? Or are these leaders afraid of something – or someone – else? Where, how and why did leadership become addicted to management systems and paperwork and lose sight of the humanistic element in the art of good management?

We'll consider whether it is possible to row back from the age of entitlement and blame culture and try to work out just why some people seek to put the blame on someone else rather than taking ownership and responsibility themselves. No manager in their right mind would ever step aside and let someone else tell them how to run their business, but managers do that all the time when it comes to the business of health and safety. Why? As the famous Dr Pepper soft drink commercial asks 'What's the worst that could happen?' In this chapter we'll explain how managers can take ownership for leading this vitally important aspect of their business.

Some of the time of course these experts will be right; there are rules and requirements which must be followed. But there will also be times when, if you do challenge, you will come to find that there is much less prescription than you might think. The freedom for you to do it your way often really does exist. In fact we'd go as far as to say that it is essential that you make your personal mark on the approach which is taken towards workplace health and safety in your organization because we're sure that the people who work there with you are all smart folks. They can sense when safety really matters and their bosses really care as opposed to when safety is being done with little or no conviction but just because the law or the experts say it must be.

Learning lessons the hard way

We now live and work in an age where change and uncertainty dominate and a 'culture of fear' is growing. The dangers and risks facing people are continually inflated and precaution is regarded as virtuous rationale for inaction when it comes to matters of safety. Heightened organizational sensitivity and 'risk anxiety' are now influencing leadership decision-making in matters of workplace safety more than ever before.

Despite enjoying unprecedented levels of safety, societies around the world today seem stunned by the ascendancy of risk consciousness and become increasingly engaged with various issues through a narrative of fear. Sustained by a culture that is anxious about change and uncertainty, modern society communicates hesitancy, and continually anticipates the worst possible outcome, discouraging people from taking risks and promoting over-precaution as a virtue. (It is worth noting that there are some businesses who take a very different approach to different types of risk – perhaps a more balanced approach to managing risks would have helped to avoid some of the financial failures the world has experienced in recent years – but that is another subject for another book.)

In the health and safety space, under the auspices of 'risk management', fear becomes institutionalized, and the fear response is encouraged and affirmed as societies move to take greater precaution to achieve more protection. Risk 'awareness' has shifted to become risk 'aversion' and a desire to eliminate risk dominates the psyche as 'Health & Safety' is proposed as salient rationale for inaction.

Despite this cultural shift for many organizations around the globe, there remain some individual leaders who are prepared to get up and make a stand. Many of these people – and indeed almost all of the most effective leaders we know in health and safety – have learned about the reality, value and importance of safety the hard way.

Learning the hard way is certainly how Andrew came to be involved in the world of health and safety. One day as a young process engineer he'd been busy in the laboratory of the Printed Circuit Board company where he worked. Andrew had analysed the solution within an operational line in the factory and concluded that a chemical addition was required to correct the mixture in a tank on the line. It was a Friday and thoughts of the weekend were running through his mind as he headed towards the chemical store to obtain what he needed. There he found his buddy George, also working on the same process line, and similarly thinking about his weekend plans. The two friends chatted easily as they filled their buckets with solutions from drums marked with various signage: a rugby match, cold beers, taking the dogs for a hike in the hills. Walking back to the line the chaps continued their chat, despite parting company and becoming separated by several metres of process equipment. As Andrew was pouring the acid from his bucket into the tank on the line, the conversation continued, although now at a higher volume to counter the noise from the factory machinery. Within a few seconds he could feel something wasn't quite right, really not quite right at all. In his distraction Andrew had not donned the protective leather apron required for additions of this particular chemical and almost the full ten litres were spilling from the bucket not into the tank but right down the front of his trousers. Looking back, it's unclear whether it was the chemical or the embarrassment of the naked dash of around one hundred metres to the emergency shower that had a stronger sting, but the lesson clearly hit home for the young engineer, and Andrew's attention has definitely been focussed on safety ever since.

But many others are not so lucky – they don't get the warning shot that Andrew did. Attend a health and safety conference anywhere around the world and you'll often find that the most persuasive speakers are those who tell their own personal story about how they came to realise how important health and safety is. They can recall the day when it all changed for them and sadly it usually involves someone getting seriously hurt or even killed.

We have the utmost admiration for these people who have learned their hard lessons and are prepared to be brave enough to stand up in front of others to reveal their mistakes in brutal honesty – in the hope that their shared words prevent just one more accident from occurring.

In the United Kingdom, Jason Anker regularly speaks to audiences at such conferences and recalls the day he fell from a ladder at work and was paralysed from the waist down by his injuries. What is extraordinary about Jason is that he doesn't blame his bosses for what happened, even though they were the ones who pressured him to do the job when he had his accident. As he propels his wheelchair onto the stage it's easy to spot the disappointment he carries on his shoulders. But, interestingly, much of Jason's anger is directed at himself – for making a bad decision and choosing to do something that he knew was unsafe. His message is very simple and resonates with each audience he speaks to: every single one of us has a choice to make about being safe – or unsafe – at work and we must each bear the responsibility for the consequences of our decisions. We've both witnessed the impact of Anker's message on shopfloor workers, but how does this apply when you are the manager rather than the worker on the front line? Well, exactly the same principle applies because as a manager you must also bear responsibility for the consequences of your actions – or inactions.

In our experience the number of managers out there who deliberately set out to put the lives of their workforce at risk are – thankfully – very much in the minority. But to be clear, there are those people who do force their workforce to take unnecessary risk or do dangerous things in order to get the job done. Some use threats of punishment or penalty if their employees don't do as they demand. Others encourage risk taking even when it is unreasonable and then ridicule those who express concern. And we're not talking about in times gone by here. These people exist right here, right now in the 21st century, and it is right and proper that the full force of criminal law should bear down on these individuals and their organizations.

Our assumption is that if you are reading this book, you are not one of these callous uncaring individuals who place no value on the lives of others and have no conscience about the consequences. Yet we also know that there are many leaders out there who aren't reading this book, and who don't take an active role in health and safety – they are simply quite happy to leave it to others to do. They recognise that the subject is important and must be properly managed, but for some reason they don't see it as part of their role. We can't help but wonder 'why not?'.

Try to imagine for one moment a production manager who regards productivity and production performance as someone else's responsibility rather than their own, as something they are quite happy to delegate to others. What an absurd idea! Or a purchasing manager who claims to be unaware that improper practices were taking place in securing contracts. Or a quality manager who views customer feedback and complaints as somehow nothing to do with him. In these and other similar cases you would be rightly minded to identify that the manager was not doing his or her job properly and was shirking their responsibilities. But as a leader not knowing or not caring what's going on in relation to health and safety in your business also means that you are not doing your job properly. You are the leader, you set the tone. The workforce looks to you and pick up signals from you on what is important – and it's not just what you say – as we mentioned previously, your people are much smarter than that.

Let us return to those who learn from experience that they need to become real leaders in health and safety. Many of those that we've met confess to having already been pretty well committed to safety before the event which changed their view, but admit that they may have been focusing on the wrong things. There are some extraordinary and inspiring stories of managers who suddenly 'get it' – but all too often because they have been personally involved in the aftermath of an incident where someone has been hurt or killed. When these incidents happen the manager is thrust forward and must deal with many things:

- **The workforce shockwave**. As workers learn that a colleague has been injured many will recognise that it could very easily have been them, perhaps on a different day in slightly different circumstances. They may well understand that what the injured person was doing was something they knew to be risky but had become accepted practice. Later in this book we'll talk more about this idea, known as the normalization of deviance.

- **Serious injury or a death**. Such an outcome will of course (for most organizations) result in a full, independent investigation by the police and / or statutory regulators – as well as whatever internal investigation is commissioned by the organization. Ongoing work is likely to be stopped whilst the incident is investigated, staff including you as the manager may be interviewed under caution.

- **Penalties and sanctions**. Formal investigations may take several weeks/months to progress. Subsequent court hearings may follow many months after the incident. During this time the possibility of prosecution will loom like a dark cloud over the organization.

There is plenty of advice out there on how to handle yourself in the event of a formal investigation process – often from lawyers keen to represent you in the courtroom. There are training sessions you can attend which will help to prepare you for the prosecution process. There are also courses that will prepare you for speaking to the media – who will almost certainly take an interest in what has happened. In today's environment any incident will find its way into the media and your customers and suppliers are bound to find out with consequent reputational damage.

As a leader, perhaps you'll handle such fallout with confidence and efficacy. After all, it's exactly this sort of ability to cope and drive forward that has got you to where you are now. But what we want to focus on here is the emotional experience of those who suddenly see their role in safety under a very different light. Those courageous managers who have stepped up to the plate after having been involved in a serious incident will speak of the worry that descends upon them as they drive towards the home of the victim. They tell of their experiences of meeting the family and sharing the terrible news. Of dealing with the distress and unease within the workforce. And their own continuous soul-searching on what more they could have done to prevent such an awful event from happening. For most of the people we've met these are things which don't go away even when the investigation concludes that there is no case for prosecution. Here is just one example of how deeply a leader was affected by a fatality that occurred on one of the sites he was responsible for. The production facility manufactured materials for the construction industry. Finished products were moved from the factory to the warehouse using forklift trucks. Trailers were then loaded from the warehouse for delivery to customers also using forklifts. The company had a good health and safety system in place, workplace transport was properly routed and controlled, pedestrians were segregated wherever possible and reasonable to do so. Despite all of those measures a fatality occurred when a loaded forklift was in collision with a new inexperienced employee during their first few weeks on the site.

The impact of this incident on the manager was so significant that he became convinced that there was an opportunity to make forklift trucks intrinsically safer. He was clear in his mind that the technology existed to install automatic stop devices in trucks that would immediately deploy the brakes if the sensor picked up any form of obstruction. The vehicle manufacturers agreed it was possible but they had never fitted those devices to any of their vehicles before for any client. Over the following few months creative thought ensued, and by the time the lease for the forklift trucks for the whole company came up for renewal the manager was able to insist that automatic stops were fitted as standard to them all.

The story doesn't end just yet. The workforce across all sites were convinced that the new safety devices would make the job slower and resistance began to build. Within weeks however, the devices were actually found to encourage steadier (not slower) driving which resulted in less collisions, less damage to product and less wear and tear on the forklift trucks. Collectively, this in turn made them more reliable and more efficient. In this case, it wasn't just workplace safety that was improved, but productivity too.

This true story underlines how a tragedy inspired someone to get up and show real leadership. There are others, and the inspiring leaders we are talking about are the ones who are prepared to stand up in front of a room full of their peers and tell the story about why they feel so passionately that doing safety is about doing the right thing. The details of the device are not what matters in this story. What matters is the passion the leader felt and the actions he drove forward to ensure that a horrible accident of the kind he had encountered on one of his sites would never, ever happen again, on his watch or into the future. He was determined to make a lasting sustainable change and was prepared to put personal energy into making it happen, even when the suppliers were less than encouraging. It's also important to note that his approach was to find a solution to the problem, not clamping down on people or procedures.

This is not an isolated example. We have heard many more equally inspirational stories. There is something about being involved in a serious incident and feeling (and accepting) that sense of responsibility that seems to foster the confidence in many of these leaders to talk about how it felt and the emotional impact it had on them personally. Tragic incidents and fatalities in particular have the same impact on those involved from other dimensions – such as the regulatory inspectors called upon to investigate what happened. Each and every one of these inspectors we've spoken to has said that they will never forget the first fatality that they were called upon to investigate; they all confirm that the experience is one that will stay with them for the rest of their lives.

Although we've encountered one or two individuals who have appeared, at least on the surface, to be able to rationalise tragedies on their watch as 'not their fault' and offer what they feel is appropriate justification for their view, it is clear that for the vast majority of managers who experience a serious safety incident at close quarters, the impact is – like for the inspectors – a long-lasting one which changes their attitude towards workplace safety. Even those who had previously seen the importance of safety at work and had felt committed before *The Big Accident* take on a markedly different and much more visible approach to leadership after the event.

In the absence of fatal accidents

In 2011, over 200 tons of butane leaked from storage tanks in Rotterdam. The tank farm, belonging to the Odfjell shipping corporation – a major global maritime player headquartered in Norway – was a major fuel terminal for the company in the Netherlands. In the subsequent investigation carried out by the Dutch Safety Board, serious deficiencies in Odfjell's approach to safety were noted. The report suggests that a poor safety culture was permitted to continue by higher leadership within the company, and reveals that many of the failings identified by the regulator were known by Odfjell managers, plans were even drawn up for their resolution, but never acted upon. Whilst the leak did not spark a fire nor cause injury, during the trial the public prosecutor remarked that the terminal in Rotterdam was *"a disaster waiting to happen"* and fined Odfjell three million Euro. This sanction hit the business hard, and despite reaching their 98th year, the company posted significant losses in year 2012. The Rotterdam terminal became the subject of a formal safety shutdown, in order to bring about the changes necessary – in safety culture, leadership, and performance. During the process, Chairman of the board, Laurence W Odfjell was interviewed by the regulatory inspectors. In his quarterly update to employees in Spring 2013 he reflected on lessons learned. Odfjell remarked that the terminal in Rotterdam had *"been too flexible in attempting to please customers"* and *"driven by sales"* and in this pursuit *"sold services we were not fully fit to perform, either from a safety or from an efficiency / reliability perspective"*. He further explained *"how difficult it* is to regain trust with any customer after a failure to deliver" and remarked that he had learned through this situation that in the modern world, blue chip companies focus sharply on health and safety performance: where a supplier does not meet the expectations of their clients in this regard, not only is reputation damaged, but the 'licence to operate' is deeply disaffected. It would appear that Odfjell certainly learned the lesson the hard way as he offers further freshly-gained wisdom:

"Some may consider safety measures as measures that add cost to operations, but we see that proper safety mindset, planning and measures reduce cost and enhance performance. Also, safety is good business simply because our reputation and balance sheet can ill afford costly incidents."

The Odfjell case brought light to the fact that safety and efficiency are not contradictory or competing forces, as Laurence Odfjell himself came to realise that:

"…only with the proper planning, mindset, assets and competence we can turn ships around efficiently in port with no compromise on safety."

What are we afraid of?

If you're reading this and now thinking to yourself "there has to be a better way than this. I'm not going to wait to learn my lesson the hard way" we're pleased that you're with us. That's what we want too. Our prime motivation in writing this book is to help more managers to find the confidence and develop the skills to lead on health and safety and to establish an organizational culture where health and safety is very firmly embedded as part of being successful. We deliberately started this chapter by describing some of the experiences of those who have learned the hard way in the hope that you will feel energised to come with us on this journey to find a better way. The point is clear; if you wait until an incident happens to you and your organization, or chance it that you will be lucky and not have it happen on your watch, the impact will be profound. Any leader who observed Tony Hayward struggling to answer questions in the aftermath of the BP Macondo incident in the Gulf of Mexico in 2010 can identify with not wanting to be in those shoes. So now we want to turn our focus to how you can lead from the front *before* that incident happens that will change your life – and the lives of many others – forever. We want to show you how to become a truly proactive leader – and to show you that it really isn't difficult.

Leading health and safety well requires many of the same skills and attributes that are required to manage other aspects of the business. No business will succeed if it is run on the basis of waiting to see what happens and reacting to events. MBAs (and many other post-graduate studies) will teach you about contingency planning, the importance of motivating people to achieve productivity, tools for improving efficiency, how to set objectives and identify key performance indicators. It will be clear, or at least implied in that training that it is for you the manager to lead on all of these processes – that is your job. You will also have been familiarised with legal reporting requirements – the need for an annual report and accounts, taxation, accounting rules and conventions. The latter will have been positioned as the framework in which you must operate, but provided you meet these requirements, you have the freedom to run your own business – to decide on the markets and the products, to decide whether to employ your own staff or outsource to contractors. Well here's the thing, it's exactly the same on health and safety. There's a legal framework which describes some of the outcomes you are expected to achieve, but how you do that is your call!

So why is it that so many managers take the opt-out route when it comes to health and safety and call in the experts to tell them how to do it? We've already explored some of the ways in which mythology plays a part in making the subject seem more complex and restrictive than it really is. Now there are many, many excellent safety people out there, but there are also people who have a vested interest in inflating risks and creating the impression that their expert guidance is desperately required. Perhaps in your own career you have encountered one (or more!) of these people. There's the 'Safety Policeman' – often they can be observed – clipboard in hand – lurking somewhere in the shadows of the shopfloor, ready to pounce on an unsuspecting victim trying to get on with their job the best they can. Or the 'Barrackroom Lawyer' who marches into board meetings to tell the executive that they must change because *"it's required under legal regulation 28b (part iii)"*. Maybe you are one of the many managers who receive multiple e-mails every week to tell you about things you must do to comply with the law and how this consultancy can solve your problems in an instant – but at a price. Or perhaps you've encountered the 'Stealth and Safety Martyr' who bangs on about the importance of doing the right thing, but then refuses to explain *how* to achieve it, instead, with suitably dramatic signs goes out of his way to do all of the H&S activities himself rather than share his knowledge with others. With this motley crew out there it's only natural that a sense of fear exists amongst business leaders, culminating in an absolute belief that this is indeed a complex subject where expert advice is essential. It isn't really surprising either when there are plenty of people telling us just that!

But let's be clear on what the law actually says. It calls on the risk creators (that's you the manager who runs the business) to identify the significant risks and to do what is <u>reasonable</u> and <u>practical</u> to manage those risks. That's it, in a nutshell.

There is no requirement to eliminate all risk – but to manage them as well as is reasonable. That means knowing what they are, what can be done to mitigate them, and knowing what your contingency plans are if the worst happens and your control measures don't work the way you expected them to.

That doesn't seem to us to be very different from what you will be doing in managing other aspects of the business, does it? Let's have a look. If you decide to launch a new product you would go through exactly the same process. You would consider the risks – what is the market demand likely to be? What are your competitor products? You would consider how to mitigate the risks – trialling the product to test the market, launching on a small scale in one area first, small production run first followed by rapid scale up if demand takes off. You would have a contingency plan for product failure – as well as knowing how you would cope if demand really takes off. Why would you have all of that in place? Because that's what good business managers do and that's what you've been taught to do. But you will also do it because your bosses will expect you to present them with plans, they will want to assure themselves that the new product launch has been properly planned and risk managed to maximise the chances of business success.

The challenge with adopting exactly the same approach to leading on health and safety is to get past the 'what could go wrong?' stage and recognise that it is just as much as part of running a successful business as managing the launch of a new product, planning a marketing campaign, recruiting new staff or any other management function. It is an integral part of everyone's job.

Managers get rewarded (and often promoted) for being positive and optimistic, for seeing opportunities, for being 'can do' people. If health and safety is seen as all about what can go wrong, it's not difficult to see why we might feel reluctant to be associated with some of that stuff. We may be perceived as being negative, or pessimistic, too cautious or unambitious either on a personal level or for the business. So let's now explore how you can throw the switch to the opposite position and become a visionary leader for workplace health and safety.

Always look on the bright side

We want you to focus on being successful – as an individual and within your business – and then to consider how you maximise the opportunities for the business itself to become (even more) successful. Along with ensuring that you recruit the right people, invest in the right equipment and so on, managing the serious health and safety risks then really does become about identifying how you can maximise the opportunities and avoid the events which could harm your valuable resources and really divert you and the business from achieving your goals. What we like about this approach is that it keeps your eyes very firmly on the successful positive reasons for integrating good health and safety practice into your business. But what it will also do is to ensure that you focus on the significant risks that really matter and avoid getting tangled up in those burdens of bureaucracy we spoke of earlier.

It should be self-evident that this approach is not about tactics and putting rules in place to deal with even the most trivial risks. It is about taking a step back, looking at the business with your eyes wide open, considering strategic risks and deciding how you want to make that an integral part of the way you run your business to achieve success. We hope that you will share our view that this approach firmly places lids on coffee cups to avoid small spills and overreacting to minor paper cuts and wasp stings in the right perspective. These are not the risks that will get in the way of achieving business success, neither do they threaten anyone's health and wellbeing in a serious way. From a safety standpoint, business success depends on keeping the workforce motivated, keeping them from harm, avoiding incidents that will interrupt or halt production. But rather than worrying about how to 'prevent accidents' we'd much rather you think about how to 'create safety' in your workplace, boosting employee awareness, morale and productivity – it makes perfect business sense, doesn't it?

We would not argue with anyone who says at this point that you should do health and safety because it is a moral obligation. Of course it is. But given that it also makes total sense in terms of business success there's now even more reason to find out what you need to do to be an great safety leader!

The 'Goal Zero' mentality

It is a normal conversation to have in any business to talk about risk appetite – but this is almost invariably in relation to financial and commercial risk. Every business must also determine its risk appetite in relation to health and safety. We acknowledge that the legal framework sets some boundaries around this – there are certain levels of risk which have been judged, quite rightly, as unacceptable and even criminal. That's what standards are for. But this is the same in the case of financial and commercial risk – standards exist and there are penalties for failure to comply.

It is important to think very carefully about risk appetite in relation to health and safety because it will determine what you and your organization chooses to do which takes you above and beyond that minimum legal standard. We think people are afraid to have these conversations because it might be misinterpreted. The converse is actually true. We talked in chapter one about the potential to create cynicism if rules are perceived as over the top. It is part of establishing the culture of every organization to be clear about levels of responsibility and authority. Every level of management must be clear about their own responsibilities and those that they are prepared to delegate.

We're not suggesting for a minute that you tell the workforce it's ok to have paper cuts and to spill coffee – but then we think that they probably already know that – they are smart people. But we do think it is reasonable to make it clear that you expect people to manage these sort of every day risks for themselves when they are at work, just as they would if they were at home – but it must be explicit, not assumed. The risks you as business leaders need to focus on and be seen to lead on are those that are created by the business. When you are seen to be operating at that level your staff will take their lead from you – as you take responsibility for the right things at your level so will they – especially if you make it clear that you expect them to take this responsibility because you trust and respect them.

Signs that say *"Caution – hot water"* above washroom taps are not treating employees as adults. Ask yourself what your own reaction would be when you see these signs. We know what ours is: *"Well of course it is – don't tell me the obvious!"*

We have come across a number of organizations who claim that *"there's no such thing as an accident, all incidents are preventable."* We could debate for a long time whether an incident-free environment sustained over long periods of time is truly achievable in every workplace. We've already said that we wholeheartedly subscribe to the view that the goal of every workplace should be to ensure that everyone goes home from work every day unharmed. In fact, we would go as far as to even suggest that the forward-thinking organizations, the ones that *truly* care about their people, might even strive to send their workers home at the end of the day in an *even better* state than they arrived to begin work that day. To have any other safety goal than keeping people safe at work would mean accepting that harm is going to occur, wouldn't it? Remember our argument about binary thinking in the earlier chapter?

As human beings we desire control. We love it. In fact, we absolutely *crave* it. It's a tiny minority who are happy to throw their hands in the air and relinquish all under the concept of *que sera, sera*. The rest of us (and that includes both of us too – well, at least most of the time!) positively feel the need to be in control of our future, our destiny, the day ahead – call it what you will. And we do everything in our power to stamp our mark on what lies ahead in the belief that we have this control. And when it comes to safety, it's easy for us – whether safety practitioners or business leaders – to colour our stamp with a 'zero' logo in the misunderstanding that that's all that we can possibly aim at, and the belief that it's infinitely achievable.

Having zero harm as a goal is fine, but let's also recognise that in a workplace where human beings interact there will – from time to time – be *incidents,* some of which are foreseeable and which we can plan for and others which are not. They kind of spring up on us. You know the phrase *'accidents happen'*? Well sometimes, yes, *sometimes* they do. And often at these times, even the very best of causation models, technical experts and simulations or modelling exercises simply come up stumped. We've got to understand that even the most perfect of systems sometimes let us down. The most competent of employees occasionally will make mistakes. The best supervisor takes their eye off the ball. Or – heaven forbid – our super-sophisticated technological monitoring system suffers a blip.

When zero just isn't quite enough

Here's another case-in-point to illustrate the performance paradox that chasing zero creates, and that a lack of understanding exacerbates. At a recent business board level monthly Operations Review meeting of a FTSE 100 multinational corporation the Director of Health & Safety provided his update:

H&S Director: *"The injury rate for this division is currently 0.18".*

Operations Vice President: *"Well, that's not very good now, is it?"*

H&S Director: *"Against a target of 0.24 for this period, it would appear that the division is progressing well and in the right direction."*

Operations Vice President: *"Perhaps, but it's not <u>really</u> zero, is it?"*

H&S Director: *"Well it's the best in our Company, and our Company leads our industry peer group by a considerable distance, and we are over 20 times better than the North American industry average."*

Operations Vice President: *"It's still deeply disappointing."*

There are many things wrong with this dialogue. Not least that the whole conversation is about numbers, rather than what actually is happening in the workplace, to whom and what can be learned for the future, but for the moment we want to concentrate on the fact that the VP thinks that 'Zero' is the only possible acceptable answer.

To be clear before we go further here: we are certainly not saying *'don't strive for a safe workplace and just sit back and put your feet up because the bad stuff will eventually happen anyway.'* The entire purpose of this book is to encourage you, the leader, to sit forward and think hard, to stand up and take the action that you feel is merited, to get out there and lead safety in the way that you believe is *just right*. But a prescriptive approach to warning people about every little thing that could possibly harm them encourages them simply to switch off their servos. To not think for themselves. To relinquish responsibility for themselves and rely on you. We want to help you create a work environment where responsibility is shared and thinking is positively encouraged. Especially the sort that's a little off the wall, or a bit outside the box.

Look, the zero harm goal doesn't have to lead to over-reaction or over-prescription – but it often does. It can also lead to fear of getting it wrong or making mistakes – and being the one who is blamed. More of that fear factor we talked about earlier. So we advocate the Goldilocks concept again here – the *'just right'* approach to 'zero harm' is to wholeheartedly embrace it as a *goal,* a vision of the future to work towards – but not a *measure* of performance. Those incidents *will* happen, they may be few and far between, or they may be many – but eventually they will come along.

Just look at the DuPont corporation – for years heralded as the 'safest company on the planet' and then their plant in LaPorte, Texas suffers a multiple fatality incident leaving four employees dead. The U.S. safety regulatory body OSHA placed the DuPont corporation on their *Severe Violator* blacklist and Assistant Secretary of Labor for Occupational Safety and Health Dr. David Michaels commented: *"These four preventable workplace deaths and the very serious hazards we uncovered at this facility are evidence of a failed safety program."* OSHA also cited DuPont for *"similar process safety management violations"* at its facilities in Darrow, Louisiana, and Deepwater, New Jersey. Following a second inspection at the LaPorte facility, OSHA found eight further violations (on top of the original 11) at the Texas plant and fined the company another $273,000, citing an *"indifference"* to creating a safe workplace – evidencing that site management didn't properly inspect equipment, implement operating procedures or have an equipment safety plan. Hitting the OSHA blacklist is bad news for any organization, whether you're an industry leader like DuPont or otherwise: once a company is added to the Severe Violator list its name cannot be removed until three years after a case is resolved.

DuPont isn't the only industrial behemoth who has learned about the shortcomings of its seemingly robust safety system the hard way. It's a similar story for BP, who celebrated 7 years without a Lost Time Injury at the Deepwater Horizon platform in the Gulf of Mexico the very day the rig exploded killing 11 people and injuring many more. The United States Chemical Safety Board was instructed to conduct a thorough investigation of the event and determined that the Deepwater Horizon incident occurred in part because BP focused their attention on personal safety issues such as worker injury rates rather than on broader safety concerns related to drilling for oil with a complex rig system. The CSB report concluded that *"BP did not have adequate controls in place to ensure that key decisions in the months leading up to the blow-out were safe or sound from an engineering perspective"* and that BP and its contracted drilling rig operator, Transocean had *"multiple safety management system deficiencies"* that led to the disaster. The response from BP to these findings was fascinating, here's an extract from their internal report:

"BP admits its managers on the oil rig could have prevented the catastrophe had they picked up warning signs … shortly before the explosion. But it places much of the blame on Transocean and Halliburton."

But the CSB weren't convinced. The board also stated that they felt BP had not learned critical lessons from previous serious events, like the March 2005 explosion at the BP Texas City refinery that killed 15 employees and injured 180 others. In their report following that incident the CSB recommended broader use of *'process safety indicators'* to improve workplace safety and reduce the likelihood of major accidents.

Learning from others

So what can we learn from these big players who get it wrong? Well, some of this will depend on where you set the bar on what gets reported – or otherwise what's known as your 'risk appetite'. But it's the response to incidents that is key. A simple test is what you feel inside. Whether your gut reaction is one of *'who is to blame for this?'*, *'it wasn't me, it was him'*, *'oh, it's not such a serious injury'* or *'what can we learn from this?'* No prizes for guessing which of these reactions we think is *'just right'*!

We may be using that fairy story analogy again here but we are well aware of the realities, we've already alluded to them in chapter 1. That *'Caution – Hot Water'* sign you put in the washrooms may be because what you are really afraid of is the claims culture that might exist within your workforce. Given what we've already said about those encouragements to make a claim that appear on TV, in hospital waiting areas and so on, it wouldn't be surprising if that were a concern. If we were in your shoes we might even feel the same.

If you take down the signs in the washrooms there may be a risk that someone may scald themselves – if the water really is that hot. But *why* is the water so hot that it could scald someone? Your caution sign isn't proper risk management – it never was. It's nothing more than a 'this-should-keep-the-lawyers-happy' knee-jerk reaction to a perception of what's happening amongst your people, and nothing more. If the water coming out of the taps in the washrooms really is hot enough to injure people – fix the problem. Would you really live with this situation at home if there was a possibility of you or your family getting scalded? After all, temperature controls are easy to install. If you don't fix the problem and take away the signs then of course there is the chance that a scalding will happen and the injured party will make a claim. But let's also recognise that your warning sign may not actually help you defend the claim. Even if the sign is there, there is every chance that you may be found liable because the water is hot enough to scald and you clearly knew about it – because you put the sign up!

So please – *please* – think about how many signs you put up. Recognise that they say more about the culture of the organization and the trust you place in your staff than your attitude to safety. If they are there because there's a real problem, fix it – that's the best way to minimise claims and to keep your staff happy.

Just right needs to apply to everything you do and say. It applies to the way you react to big events as well as how you approach smaller and seemingly less important issues such as signage.

We are going to talk a lot more about how to create the right culture in the following chapters but we hope that what you are seeing now is at least the glimmer of a possibility of starting to take some of those courageous decisions to walk away from the over-prescriptive approach and start to think about workplace safety for yourself. Even if the small steps are just the washroom signs and water temperature.

If the safety culture is *just right*, if the organization is focussed on success and success includes not having serious incidents which harm employees and interrupt production, performance will be good, morale will be good, there will be learning as opposed to blame and those claims should certainly be less frequent.

All too difficult?

Somehow modern society has created a scenario where too many managers regard health and safety as too difficult or too complex. We've shown earlier how this can change if a manager has direct experience of a serious incident. For those for whom it hasn't happened yet we sincerely hope that you don't ever have to go there. Instead, over the following chapters we'll help you to create the ability to think about – and to feel what it might be like – if the worst were to happen – not so that you become fearful of such an event or paralysed like a rabbit caught in the headlights. We want you to be able to recognise just how much is at stake – for you, for your staff and for the business. It really does make good business sense for you as the manager to lead on health and safety – and the workforce will recognise and respect you for it, if it is genuine and heartfelt.

We believe that the single most important issue is to care about your workforce – the rest will follow. Management training in the 70's and 80's was focussed very much on people – good managers needed to get to know their staff as individuals, to understand how to motivate them, to explain what was important and why things mattered. Right back at the heart of being a good manager was the practice of being human and good, solid personal interaction.

Perhaps it's not surprising that in some parts of the world, management training in 'being human' has come back after many years of industrial unrest and conflict. Thankfully it isn't all about being nice and friendly and having cosy chats: this type of training is about using systematic approaches to doing tasks effectively which include how to communicate to staff, and how to motivate and engage them so that they feel part of the team.

Systematic approaches by managers then leads us on to the creation of management systems. Looking back, it appears that in some cases some of that human behaviour stuff and understanding people got lost along the way. Management systems have taken over in lots of ways – they now standardise the way in which tasks must be done. We can feel Goldilocks' presence creeping in here again because it's all about keeping the right balance. Management systems are helpful when they are used in the right way which is to support the human processes – but let's be sure we get the balance *just right* – and that means that people are involved in agreeing what the standard approaches will be, the procedures truly reflect how the job is done in practice and the consequences of not doing it according to the procedure are properly explained. But just like risk assessments (which after all are just part of the management system), if the whole system has become bound up in volumes of paperwork – it will be a drag on the system not a help. If there is no mechanism for people to suggest better ways of doing things which can be reviewed and incorporated quickly and easily into the system then it's a drag not an enabler. If the system places requirements on people which are unreasonable and create temptation to take short cuts (without explaining why it's important) then short cuts will occur no matter what the system says – because that's what humans do!

As a rule of thumb, good management systems are the ones that allow thinking, encourage people to come up with improvements and which incorporate new and good ideas to help the business to be more successful. Bad management systems are ones which overprescribe and which insist on compliance with a set way of doing things – even when your smart staff know there is a better and more effective way.

Management systems can be very good tools if they are used intelligently. There are many other tools to help manage health and safety but – just like those super-tech cars we mentioned earlier – they all need intelligent users. And that means you! Performance measures are a very good example of the tools of the health and safety trade but there are many others. We see lots of examples of them being used but often in the wrong way or inappropriately (look again at the debate earlier in this chapter about safety performance numbers). Injury frequency rates are reported by just about every organization who claims to be serious about health and safety. They can be helpful if they are being used to measure improvement from year to year or to compare similar operations around the world in a multinational company – providing they reflect the real world. For many organizations we have seen and worked with though, these LTI charts (Lost Time Injury rate) have become LGI charts – or *'Looking Good Indexes'* created and shared only to bolster spirits, foster false hope, encourage misguided confidence, and, even at their most simplistic, keep up with the Joneses.

But small companies will find them very confusing – especially if they use the data to try to compare themselves with other much larger and dissimilar organizations – and that is what does happen! We haven't done with the tools of the trade yet. In fact, we are going to devote a whole chapter to choosing and using the right tools for management, but at this stage on the journey we simply want to make the point that minding your own business includes choosing which tools will work for you – not mindlessly copying everyone else or making meaningless comparisons.

In closing

In this chapter we have tried to explore a different paradigm where health and safety becomes an integral part of doing business well. We've illustrated how often this paradigm shift happens to managers who have learned the hard way when they have been involved in a very serious incident which has deeply affected them (often for the rest of their lives) and we have explored why there is every reason to avoid this scenario and become the leader to whom the worst never happens. We've argued that good health and safety is about focusing on success not failure or blame.

We've challenged you to think about the fears that cause us to hand off health and safety to someone else and questioned why this is the case when so many other aspects of management are clearly recognised as the domain and responsibility of the manager. But we've also raised some questions about managing the right things and being prepared to delegate other aspects to generate responsibility and positive culture.

We've also suggested that it's time we put the human element back into health and safety, recognising management systems and other tools as just that – tools to help us but not to become the ends in themselves.

We hope that you are starting to see that there is a real possibility of making this new paradigm a reality and a force for good – in health and safety terms and for business success. But it's over to you now – are you up for *minding your own business*?

You made it through to the end of the second chapter, well done! Just like last time, we have some questions we'd like you to reflect on:

1 Do you know anyone who has experienced a serious incident in their company? Have you talked to them about their experience? If not yet, now's the time to grab some coffee and go talk.

2 Is your business in the *'caution* signs everywhere' mode, stating the obvious? What do the workforce think about this approach? Do they

even see the signs?

3 Is the integral nature of health and safety and business success something that you already recognise or are you still seeing it as a barrier or burden? How does the rest of your management team view it?

4 What part do management systems play in your organization? Are you sure that they reflect reality? Do they encourage improvement and innovation?

There is in the worst of fortune the best chances for a happy change.

Euripedes, Greek dramatist

CHAPTER 3

Mindset over Matter – Getting Your Culture *Just Right*

Complex attitudes live in the boardroom and encourage and shape (and in some cases even force) leaders to take the decisions they do When it comes to the matter of safety in the boardroom we know that many leaders just do whatever the safety manager advises or tells them to do. Is this effective persuasion? Well no, at least some decisions, we suspect, are driven by fear. Fear of prosecution or civil litigation. Fear of insurance policies not covering a liability because recommendations haven't been followed to the letter. Fear of… the unknown. Fear is certainly a key element but we'd argue that it's not the only factor at play. It may also be about – for some at least – a fundamental lack of knowledge on what to do and how to do it, or a failure to recognise that good health and safety is integral to good business.

In recent times, growing ranks of practitioners have become masters of the black art of 'stealth and safety' but we can't help but wonder why some strive to make things so complex. And when it comes to workplace safety why do so many business leaders choose to hand everything over to a team of so-called experts rather than owning and managing it themselves? Is it because these experts have told the leaders it's so complex they can't possibly understand it, let alone do it? Where, when and how did modern business become addicted to management systems and the generation of copious quantities of paperwork? How did we lose sight of the human part of managing and leading workplace safety? How can we as leaders know what's good enough? And how do <u>you</u> decide what is *just right* for your organization?

In this chapter we'll explore some of the contemporary challenges in workplace safety, returning again to the (over-)use of safety signage and reliance on personal protective equipment to the dichotomies of defining accidents and incidents. We'll consider the burgeoning tide that has become the 'big data' of safety and offer ideas on how to avoid getting caught in the current. We'll also propose (and emphatically encourage) a shift in both your perspective and your mindset, explain how we can look without seeing and also see only what we're looking for. And in recognition of the fact that no-one is perfect, we'll also offer some suggestions for getting the most out of things when it all goes wrong and an accident does occur.

Getting workplace safety *just right*

Judith says that one of the greatest privileges of her former job as Chair of Great Britain's safety regulator, the *Health & Safety Executive*, a role she held for a period of 8 years until Spring 2016, has been the opportunity to visit many different companies and operations, the length and breadth of Britain and in many other parts of the world. It's a privilege that Andrew shares and appreciates too in his role as a consultant working with organizations around the globe.

Whether we're in the United Kingdom or the United States, Azerbaijan or Australia, South Africa or Switzerland, Russia or Romania, Colombia or China there's nothing quite like putting your kit on, getting out there to where the action is, and truly seeing just what exactly is going on. On such visits to site we've both noticed that it's surprisingly easy to get a sense of which companies have managed to find the *'just right'* approach to health and safety and recognise those who are not yet quite in the right place – either because they are doing too much or too little.

Signs of the times

You might have picked up on our rather negative start to this chapter already. We apologise for starting a little grumpily, but we do feel that there's a dilemma for business leaders here that needs to be explored. It's the 'elephant in the room'. Despite our initial criticism of some safety practitioners, there are many who are 'on the case'. They are trying to do their best in your organization, but in the absence of clear leadership from you, the boss, they may go 'over the top'. One of the hallmarks of this may be fastened to almost every fixed surface and immovable object. Yes, safety signage is everywhere.

'Mind the gap', 'Watch the step', 'Hold the handrail', 'Caution slippery floor', 'Hot surface', 'Look out for vehicles', 'Danger don't touch' …

The list is endless and they can be found wherever you look. What this tells us is that *someone* has done a safety review and identified lots of hazards. The expert has seen the hazards, but is either not sure of how to get them fixed or fears that she will be seen as a problem if she asks for them to be fixed. So, her solution is to make sure that everyone is aware of the hazards by putting up signs to warn them. *"What's wrong with that?"* you may be thinking. Well, several things really. Here are just three questions to get you thinking:

1 **Should some of these hazards be removed or managed rather than warning people about the danger?**
We've already explored the *'Caution Hot Water'* example in the previous chapter. The same argument goes for slippery floors, hot surfaces and vehicle risks. In many of these cases simple measures could and should be put in place to remove the hazard, not just whack up a few signs and hope for the best.

2 **Do people really take notice of these signs anyway?**
They certainly don't if the place is festooned with them. They become overwhelmed by the amount of signage and fall into a state of 'sign blindness' – unable to discern the real risks that they must avoid from the minor hazards. When the signs first go up, they may be noticed for a few days but after a while they become part of the furniture and blur away into the background. As your employees focus on their main duties, the risk of what psychologists call inattentional blindness kicks in. Workers become so dedicated to their task that they simply fail to notice or even think about the risks the signs warn them against[1].

3 **What's the motivation for putting them up?**
In some cases the signs are installed to ensure that if anyone does encounter the hazard then they will be unable to make a civil claim against the organization because they had *'been warned of the risk'* – but as we've already discussed this is by no means clear cut – the sign is clear evidence that the organization knows there is a danger. A far better way to insulate the organization from claims is to do the job properly to begin with – conduct your risk assessment, communicate the findings, fix the hazards where and when it is reasonable to do so and work hard to encourage a culture where people watch out for themselves and each other.

Gearing up

But it's not just the signs of our times when it comes to misunderstood workplace safety measures; the ubiquitous use of protective clothing is another commonly encountered feature. Often we see large-scale distribution of hard hats or other PPE for *everyone*. *"It's simpler to control and easier to see who's not wearing them"* we're told by the over-zealous (and perhaps under-thinking) safety officer, but really the only thing that's easy is the way in which your supplier continues to receive order after order from your firm for these items.

Safety gear is important of course – when the right equipment is specified on the basis of risk – but we really do question its use in blanket fashion. In the same way that we've already spoken about the overuse of signage, the same problem applies to Personal Protective Equipment. Steel toecap boots for *everyone*. Even the office clerk as he walks back from the toilets around the edge of the warehouse to his office needs to put them on. Same for the manager who wants to go out into the yard and visit her team. And those visitors on a site tour following the yellow-painted pedestrian walkways. No wonder your supplier loves you.

Conversely, we have seen great examples of where areas of factories have designated areas where one can walk through without safety shoes or hard hats, but with clear designation of when you enter an area where they must be worn. We think this is a great example of being proportionate and getting it *'just right'*.

Nice to see you, to see you…

And it's the same with high visibility jackets, isn't it? The staple of

Personal Protective Equipment (PPE) is applied throughout modern industry right across the world. The purpose of these vests and jackets is to make people visible – to stand out from the crowd. This certainly works well on the pedestrian zebra crossing near Andrew's home, where the lady with her lollipop strides out and stops traffic with just a glint of her neon. But in a workplace yard, factory shop-floor or distribution warehouse their purpose may be defeated if no one stands out. We can understand why everyone needs to be visible in a warehouse, or anywhere there is interaction of people and vehicles. But also recognise that the overuse of hi-viz in all areas all of the time defeats the purpose because no one stands out, everyone looks the same – even if the colour chosen is the loudest and brightest shade you can find.

As we just said in the previous paragraph, when we get so focused on our tasks we simply don't see the things we've become over familiar with. Consider a warehouse or yard area within your workplace – pedestrians, trucks and forklifts moving around. A common idea to improve safety is to have all the pedestrians wear hi-viz vests, it intuitively feels like the right thing to do – they become more distinctive. But if the drivers are not *looking* for pedestrians, they won't see them. Hi-viz doesn't guarantee them being noticed – on their own they don't solve the problem. When the vests become a little dirty or tired through regular washing, they can often blend in even more easily with the colours on your forklift trucks, warehouse racking systems, and lorry curtains too. Hi-viz jackets or not, the key is to ensure that your warehouse operators are alert to the risks and are looking out for all people who may be in the area – expected or not.

In Australia, it's mandatory for trainee and newly-qualified motor-bikers to wear hi-viz vests. But Professor Richard Huggins, Chair of Statistics at the University of Melbourne and also a biker who was hit by a car whilst he was wearing a hi-viz vest reviewed several studies on motorcycle conspicuity and *'look but fail to see'* accidents concluded that there is *'such sufficient doubt'* of the effectiveness of hi-viz that he argues the law should be repealed. Huggins goes further to suggest that the actual wearing of high visibility clothing may impart a false sense of security in the wearers – particularly in novice motorcycle riders. Could the same sense of invincibility through a reliance on thinking that wearers are ultra-visible permeate the workplace? We think it just might.

Meanwhile, in the United Kingdom, the Institute of Advanced Motorists released a report in January 2016 that considers the use of high visibility vests by motorcycle riders. As a biker, Andrew read on with interest. The IAM concludes the same as Professor Huggins: your bright yellow, orange or even pink vest doesn't mean you'll be seen. The report was silent on the impact of those fuzzy animal ears that some bikers choose to stick on their helmets. Whilst we've both noticed many of these over the last few months the jury is still out on their purpose and efficacy!

Look, the reality is that we see far less of what's going on than we think. When we devote our attention to a particular area or aspect of our visual world, we tend not to notice unexpected objects appearing even when they're right in front of our noses! When it comes to safety the illusion of attention coupled with the over-reliance on signage and PPE is a big issue that we really must get to grips with.

A question of ownership

We have both encountered far too many managers for whom safety is about doing what others *tell them* they have to do. For some this is described as *'the burden of regulation'* – the need to comply with the law, with rules and regulations *imposed* by others – whether state department, industry regulator, or safety expert. The outcome of this 'burden' mentality is that the manager himself or herself does not see or fully understand the need for these rules. It also further implies that measures are required which carry a cost and for which there is little or no benefit.

Depending upon where in the world you are as you are reading this book it is likely that there are rules in place which you don't understand the need for. But in many places, starting with the United Kingdom and adopted throughout the Commonwealth nations and in many other countries around the world 'goal based regulations' exist to set minimum standards and to regulate safety in the workplace. These regulations should not result in unnecessary and costly measures; in fact, the whole idea, indeed the very basis of the legislation is that risks should be managed in a way that is reasonable and sensible[2]. In simple terms, as we've already suggested earlier in this book, that means that a more rigorous approach will be required in high hazard businesses than in those of relatively low risk. So as a leader, if the rules you are being told that you have to comply with don't make sense to you or for your business, stop and think and try to find out whether they really apply to you or not. It's time to be brave, to step up and challenge, and to build greater clarity and consensus of just what's needed.

Similarly, we know of business leaders who do things for safety because they are *advised* by others that it's necessary. In this case, these 'others' may include people like insurance brokers and corporations or their risk assessors who will be looking for way to reduce their financial risk exposure in underwriting your business – but it is always worth remembering that their perspective is not the same as yours. You see things from a different angle. It is worth asking what will happen if you *don't* implement their recommendations – especially if they seem costly and highly risk averse to you. It is by no means a given that failure to follow their advice will invalidate your whole cover – they may choose for example to increase the premium if the measures are not implemented, in which case it is for you to weigh up the additional premium cost versus the cost of putting the measures in place. Another possibility may be that they will expect you to increase the level of excess on the policy – again a financial decision for you to take about your business. Just like Goldilocks and her porridge, it's about getting the mix *just right* for you and your business. When you rely on someone else cooking things up and serving it to you as *they* prefer don't be surprised if it doesn't taste good to you.

Advice may also come from those growing ranks of practitioners we mentioned earlier, some of whom may be within your own organization or they may be external consultants that you have engaged to provide you with expert advice in an area where you feel it's difficult to know where to start. Let us say up front that there are a lot of very good health and safety practitioners out there, who do a really good job of supporting managers in putting the right measures in place. But *'right'* and *'good'* must of course be defined. 'Good' does not mean 'expert' in legislation unless that knowledge is accompanied by a confidence and competence to interpret the requirements of the law in a sensible and proportionate way. The right measures will be determined by you and your business. Given that we've already said this is about creating the right culture (more of this to come in the next chapters) it follows that one size most definitely does not fit all. Whether measures are right for you and your business or not will depend on the nature of the workforce (consider factors such as numbers of employees, age range, experience, diversity, competence and capability), the workplace (plant, processes and equipment, environmental issues such as noise, lighting and hygiene) and your organization (strategy, culture, stability, values, location in the world) and a whole variety of other factors.

The clues in your culture

Let's take a detour for a moment to briefly explore one of these factors, perhaps the most important one in our opinion, (though remember you don't have to agree with everything we – or anyone else – says!) and that's culture.

Whilst every single person on this planet has his or her own unique personality, history, experiences and interests Dutch social psychologist Geert Hofstede[3] asserts that *"all people share a common human nature."* He continues:

"Our shared human nature is intensely social: we are group animals. We use language and empathy, and practice collaboration and intergroup competition. But the unwritten rules of how we do these things differ from one human group to another."

We can call these unspoken expectations, together with the unwritten rules and norms of behaviour that exist in group setting, *'culture'*. Hofstede explains that:

"…culture provides moral standards about how to be an upstanding group member; it inspires symbols, heroes, rituals, laws, religions, taboos, and all kinds of practices – but its core is hidden in unconscious values that change at a far slower rate than the practices."

Groups may be formed around national, religious, ethical or ethnic beliefs, but can also be based on a particular occupation (such as a Chartered Engineer); academic discipline (Doctors, Fellows); school, college or university, (graduates, alumni); industry or sector; sexuality; family history (clans) and even style of fashion (punks, rockers, mods, or 1970s bell-bottoms anyone?). Each group or culture will have its own core values that shape the behaviours of and bond together its members. Bear in mind that today, in a world that's more interconnected and effectively 'smaller' than ever before it's possible to belong to several groups at the same time.

It is vital when weighing up what's right for your business to fully understand the varying culture(s) of your employees and the groups to which they belong. Otherwise, we just won't be able to get things done. So let's work through a couple of practical examples.

In some parts of the world it is solidly ingrained within the culture to obey instructions from people who are more senior without challenging them. In China for example, the national culture tends to accept that inequality within groups (such as in organizations) exist, that an official hierarchy is necessary, and that leaders – whilst often appearing inaccessible – are entitled to hold such privileges. The behaviours that result from this culture are often pragmatic, demonstrating perseverance and not just tolerance but an acceptance of change. Groups are usually tightly-knit and an intrinsic expectation that relatives and group members will look after each other in return for unwavering loyalty. There can be such a palpable strength in relationships, though, that the task of work can be relegated to that of lesser importance.

By comparison in the United States of America the sense of need for hierarchical structure is vastly reduced as the prevailing belief is one of equal rights. This can manifest as a positive drive towards minimising inequality and the door to the supervisors office always being open. On the flip side, this broader equity and higher level of individualism demands quick results when it comes to work and fosters a *'Git-'er-done'* mentality of fast action and adequate results.

Responding to behavioural norms and group cultures in the way you lead and manage on safety is crucial. The challenge for us as leaders today is not just in communicating within and across these groups and cultures, but indeed the practice and development of our own intercultural cooperation skills and the subtle encouragement of the same in others. Provide safety rules to one culture and the result may be successful if they are good rules. But in another culture even the best rules may still be challenged and could even be less likely to be adhered to. If you find yourself here, don't despair, dig deeper into the cultural clues you can find and explore whether an alternative less prescriptive and more inclusive approach might help you make better progress.

This is one very important aspect of bringing the human element back into managing health and safety that we mentioned earlier and we believe it is absolutely crucial.

So far in this chapter we've highlighted the challenge of boards and senior leaders feeling paralysed by the experts and finding themselves doing just what they are told to do – even if they're not sure why they are doing it. In some companies we have encountered this is reinforced by both the structure and the culture of the organization. Here, health and safety is managed by a separate group of people with little or no connection to the rest of the business – it's a 'bolt-on', a dotted-line to HR, a subset of Operations, a devolved office. We would be the first to agree that some form of independent assessment and challenge –

just like internal audit on other business activities – is a good thing in any business. But the problem in health and safety comes when the separated part of the organization is the delegated responsibility for managing safety. These experts can be advisors, auditors or facilitators. They can influence behaviours and help shape beliefs. But the ownership and leadership can never be transferred to them – that has to stay with the line management so that it is truly an integral part of the business.

The world of paper and the world of work

In some organizations, often those where responsibility for safety has been devolved to a Health & Safety Department, the actual management of health and safety at work is all about the paperwork. Many such organizations are proud of their management systems – and some rightly so – but we've also visited many locations where the paperwork is produced almost for the sake of it – not because it is needed. Some of this will be because a manager has felt he or she cannot assess the risks on their own and have called on outside expertise to help them. This in turn has led to a consultant selling them a complex off the shelf management system which is neither appropriate nor proportionate to the risks in that business. The organizational love affair with management systems has created a paper shield which generates a degree of false comfort for managers today, but really only serves to distance us from those we need to work with – our staff – the human beings who may be affected adversely by their work. We've seen countless health and safety management systems in ring binders on shelves gathering dust, never having been looked at since the day the consultant produced them. And then there are those which are dragged down from the shelves every time something goes wrong. Policies and procedures are updated, new detailed sub-sections added, and Document Change Notes sent off for filing. Yet when we take one of these tomes from the shelf and go compare it to what's happening on the shop-floor we see two parallel universes: the *Paper World* and the *Real World*. And very often we observe that the leaders in control have absolutely no idea that there's a difference.

Without doubt some paperwork is necessary. The establishment of a solid health and safety management system is a key step towards reducing accidents and building a sensible approach to managing risk – but the system is about much more than paperwork. In order for it to be effective, however, you need to ensure that safety considerations are woven into the fabric of the business activities at every level. For this to be achieved, everyone working in the organization needs to clearly understand the importance of safety at work, their specific personal role and responsibilities in achieving and assuring a safe workplace, and, ultimately, the value placed on this by you as a leader, and the organization at large. As we said earlier, the management system is a tool to help achieve the goal, not an end in itself.

Big data

It's all about the data these days. In their brilliant book *The Age of Context*, Robert Scoble and Shel Israel suggest that the amount of data we have for any given thing is now so vast that to try to define it in quantifiable terms is *"like trying to measure the universe or calculate how many angels can dance on a pinhead."* They illustrate this point well with a flashback to the internet. In 2005, Google CEO Eric Schmidt suggested the size of the net to be 5 million terrabytes. In 2014, the growth of the web had become exponential, with Israel and Scoble estimating that the internet expands at a rate of 2.5 million terrabytes <u>per day</u>. In more comprehensible terms they point out that this means that more data is now being uploaded to the internet every day than has been previously created throughout the recorded history of the world we live in. Very big data indeed.

Nowadays we are able to collect much more data and at a much higher velocity than ever before. 90% of data that exists today didn't exist three years ago. There are organizations who make their business on the creation of this big data, constructing ever-more complex systems for mining the information from and for corporations around the globe. 'Big data' is as its name suggests is a tag given to the accumulation of numbers that many large organizations seem to have become accustomed to in this modern, interconnected world. But the key to all of this data is knowing how to utilise it and turn it into helpful and *meaningful* information. Bigger is unlikely to be better when it comes to safety, especially if it adds more layers of complexity or if it is used inappropriately.

This trend for big data has certainly affected the safety world. Traditionally workplace safety has been measured in terms of accidents that occur. We've long held a fascination with the numbers, from recording the numbers of accidents we've had, to simple analysis showing where the accidents have occurred – geographically, physically and anatomically. The number of injuries that were sustained are counted up and logged onto a chart. To show the impact on our operations, safety advisors might typically take the latest 'cost of accidents' – which depending on your sources could be up to £20,000 for a significant injury – and multiply this by the number of accidents in a given period. Putting some context around that figure, Health & Safety Executive ('HSE') estimate that uninsured losses associated with an accident at work are at least ten times the value of any insurance premiums paid. In its own right, this data may be persuasive enough to encourage some leaders to take action.

But other leaders no doubt were keen to see how their organization's performance fared against the bigger picture. So from here things evolved to setting the data into context, by running the actual accident numbers through a formula based on the number of hours or days worked by the workforce. Now we have Accident Frequency Rates. The benefit of such rates is obvious: it becomes possible to compare and contrast. Departments can be cross-checked against their performance in safety. An organization may compare itself to its peers or competitors, or against an industry or sector average rate. It's important when using rates to be clear on how they are calculated, as variation exists between sectors and regions. For example, in the United Kingdom frequency rates are typically calculated by dividing the number of accidents in a fixed period (e.g. one year) by the number of hours worked in the period and then multiplying this figure by 1,000,000. In the United States frequency rates tend to be the sum of the number of injuries sustained, multiplied by 200,000 and then divided by the number of hours worked. Before comparing your rates with those of others, be sure to know which protocol each party is using. Be careful also about any conclusions you draw from the comparison. One incident or injury in a small company or division will have a major impact on the numbers compared to one incident in a large organization. What do you know about the workforce, the culture, the management? Remember that all of these things matter. And they matter a lot.

The diversification of accidents and the performance paradox

Alongside the interest in measuring safety through frequency rates, additional event categories have been introduced. Accidents are no longer simply 'major' or 'minor', they could be split further into Lost Time, Lost Workday, Restricted Work Duty, Medical Treatment, First Aid

Treatment, and of course, in the worst case, Fatalities. As each category has been added to the list more and more data has been gained. But despite the breadth and depth of data, we're still essentially measuring <u>failure</u>. Accidents by their very nature are the result of holes in our system. Holes due to human, technological, systemic or cultural failure – or a combination of several

This fascination with failure is in itself puzzling. Where else in our operations do we calculate 'successful performance' by counting the number of times we fail and then endeavouring to fail *less*? We don't restrict ourselves to measuring the quality of the products we create by counting the number of times our customers complain. We don't measure productivity solely from the number of hours our machines sit idle. And HR doesn't conclude employee engagement levels just from the number of days workers are absent on sick leave – and they certainly don't make the mistake of trying to fix engagement by driving down sickness absence.

But then again, failure is data-rich. Take aviation as an example, the 'black box' flight recorder installed in almost all commercial jets constantly records data on pilot decisions and actions, velocity, altitude and much, much more. In the event of a plane crash, authorities and experts can spend weeks poring over every last shred of evidence from that little black box.

The performance paradox we have in safety can be challenging. On one hand we have the human desire to prevent harm and we set off in pursuit of achieving zero accidents. Whilst on the other, each step we make in moving closer to achieve our target of zero continues to highlight how we have failed. The gut reaction is that we are not doing enough and more must be done. But more of what? Is it conceivable that we are doing the wrong things and need to do less of them? So how can we make more positive progress?

The value of the near miss

Over the last decade or so safety managers have reminded their employers of the important work of Herbert Heinrich, an insurance company man, who back in the 1950s reviewed thousands of accident reports received by his company and concluded a relationship between the numbers of serious accidents and those events that almost led to an accident -what we know now as *Near Misses*. Heinrich used his data to construct a model where serious and fatal accidents sit at the top of a pyramid with a significantly larger volume of less serious accidents beneath. Heinrich posited that for each major injury there would be 10 minor injuries and a further 300 negative incidents where no injury was sustained[4]. The theory suggested that if we could reduce the number of Near Misses sustained in the workplace then this would have a dramatic and positive impact on the other more serious categories of incident in turn – First Aid Treatment, Medical Treatment, Lost Time, and, ultimately Fatal accidents.[5]

Following this plausible hypothesis, organizations around the globe prioritized the identification of Near Misses. Managers were set targets, which they cascaded down through their teams and the hunt for Near Misses in every workplace began in earnest. We know of many companies who, armed with the best of intentions – and of course the mandatory clipboard and check-sheet – went forth to multiply the numbers of these 'Almost Accidents' in their workplace. For some organizations, the act of finding Near Misses seems to compete neck and neck with the aim of getting their product manufactured and off the line, with employees being required to spend increasing amounts of time on the hunt.

One Fortune 500 global manufacturing company we know even went as far as setting a formal target of five Near Misses per worker each week. The logic behind the activity appeared sound – *"we want our employees to be more mindful, to tell us when they see things that could cause harm"* – but the resulting pressure for the employees to *find* things that often they could not see became destructive as more and more workers were hauled in for questioning by their supervisor after *'failing to meet their Near Miss targets'*. Beyond the ill-feeling spreading fast through the workforce, the data being gathered was certainly big. On a good day (assuming Near Miss targets were achieved) there could be upwards of twelve thousand Near Miss Reports filed. Some on paper (for those without access to a computer, or for people in a hurry), some electronically through a specially designed computer system. The paper forms were physically collected from Near Miss Boxes positioned around the factory floors by members of the safety team and nominated Workplace Safety Champions (operators selected to take time away from their normal duties to support safety activities) and taken to central locations to be manually entered to the online database. From here emails were despatched to department supervisors and managers to flag the events that had been reported. Managers would leap into action, often assembling cross-functional teams to resolve the issues flagged to them, taking pride at then being able to return to the system and officially close out their Near Miss reports.

For this organization, each Near Miss was viewed as incredibly valuable data and treated accordingly. Every week a chart was created for each work area showing whether it had achieved its requisite target, including the actual number of Near Misses recorded and showing what proportion of the Near Misses identified had been rectified so as not to present further risk. The charts were discussed at team talks, board meetings and divisional conferences. The additional resources, necessarily hired as Data Analysts to interpret the vast volume of numbers were regarded by many operational folks as demi-Gods, frequently treated to cups of coffee, doughnuts and kind words. But what of the impact on safety performance you might ask. And rightly so. After the initial rush of 'finding and fixing' workplace hazards, the organization failed to notice that the law of diminishing returns was taking its toll. So focused on the numbers, the corporate culture had evolved into one that was now system obsessed. For many very senior leaders everything hung on those Near Miss targets. But sadly, after the initial positivity, the concerted focus did not deliver the expected improvement in safety performance, as one might expect from the hypothesis. At the same time someone remarked that productivity and efficiency metrics were dropping. The economic downturn and a shift in the marketplace were quickly offered as rationale. Could it rather be that over-zealous targeting of Near Misses had actually caused the business to *generate* Near Misses of an ever more trivial nature rather than identifying and focusing on the real ones? And could this activity in turn generate a negative impact on other aspects of the organization? We'll leave it for you to run the numbers here and draw your own conclusion[6].

But in the age of context, just logging Near Misses is not enough. Surely we could create bigger data from this category? Enter the concept of *High Potential Low Frequency Injury* and its junior sibling the *Low Potential High Frequency Injury* and the opportunity for *even more* data.

Big data or big black hole?

We can't help but wonder if the trend for big data is beginning to detract focus from the importance of ensuring a safe workplace. Invited to sit in on the monthly board meeting of a multinational utilities firm recently Andrew was intrigued by the first agenda item entitled '*Safety Data*

Review'. For the next 30 minutes the company safety manager presented no less than 34 PowerPoint slides, each containing a minimum of one chart or graph, and many slides offered two, three or more. During the presentation the assembled executives appeared to be in varying states of discomfort, misunderstanding, oblivion, confusion, frustration, and at times, bemusement. Despite this the summation of this section of the meeting (along the lines of *'We're heading in the right direction, aren't we?'*) was met with sage nods of agreement, approval, and positive mumblings. When the safety leader left the room the collective sigh of relief was palpable. Several hours later at the end of the board meeting, Andrew chatted with the leaders. It quickly became apparent that not one of them understood the charts and graphs presented by the safety manager. None of them were able to recall the current accident frequency rates, let alone define their calculation. It appeared that not one of the executives felt they could admit to this in front of the safety professional – or their peer group – so the simpler route for each of them was to offer support and continue the pursuit of their corporate target of getting to zero workplace accidents. It was clear: big data had slayed all enthusiasm for safety.

Just consider for a moment how much better it might have been if this conversation had started with the board asking the safety manager to tell them what the biggest risks were in that organization and to explain how they were being managed effectively. We'll come back to this point shortly, hold tight.

But don't just take our word for it, that these conversations really do take place in boardrooms around the world. The United States Chemical Safety & Hazard Investigation board report on the explosion which occurred at BP's Texas City refinery in 2005 noted that a reliance on personal injury rate data had failed to provide a true picture of process safety performance. Further, such data was not a useful indicator of health and safety culture at the plant. Former US Secretary of State James Baker III led the investigation panel which concluded that *"BP did not set an appropriate safety tone at the top or establish appropriate (safety) goals and expectations."*

Just five years later, on 20th April 2010, BP hit the headlines again when the Deepwater Horizon oil drilling platform suffered a series of explosions which turned the rig into a fireball killing 11 and injuring many more. Just hours before the disaster, senior leaders had visited the rig to celebrate seven years without a Lost Time Injury. A report by the Centre for Catastrophic Risk Management concluded there that *"BP's organizations and operating teams did not possess a functioning safety culture. Their system was not propelled towards the goal of managing maximum safety in all its manifestations but was rather geared towards a trip and fall compliance mentality rather than being focused on the big picture."*

What we see depends on what we look for

Back in the 1800s, English philanthropist and biological scientist John Lubbock uttered these simple words, yet more than a century and half later they continue to resonate with us.

This quotation is an important reminder for us to be mindful of our perspective as leaders. When it comes to safety it's easy to see the negatives, the accidents, the failures, the poor behaviours – isn't it? To fret about the number of times accidents occur, to vow to avoid recurrence, and to invoke measures designed to control risks. It's easy to measure the number of accidents, and even easier to be convinced that a downward trend-line is indicative of improving performance. And why not? After all, it's how many organizations have been doing safety for years. But safety performance should never be confused with accident rates.

So what's your perspective? What do you look for? Do you see good safety performance as an absence of evidence of failure? Do you jump to attention each time a worker is injured and invest lots of time and effort in safety then? Do you compare your data against that of peers in the hope that in some peculiar competition you are deemed to have failed less than they?

When we look for failure, it is, of course, what we'll see. Neurologists and psychologists alike tell us our brains are hard-wired to do it. And in the pressurized climate of modern business we have come to expect people to do their jobs well, so that when there's a failing, it's even easier to spot. But declining Accident Frequency Rates are like a two-legged stool – you can balance on it for so long but eventually you're going to topple over.

Learn from failure, then flip your perspective

So we propose an alternative. Instead of the traditional emphasis on counting up the number of accidents and aiming for zero we'd like you to consider using your mindset over matter and flip your perspective. We'd like you to go beyond 'preventing accidents' and focus on the notion of 'creating safety'. Yes, *creating* safety. Just in the same way as your organization creates high quality products, or creates excellent customer service we believe that creating a safe place of work is just as important to business success – and the benefits will far outweigh any costs. Whether you're making toothpaste or car parts, drilling for oil or mining for gold, building tower blocks or computer systems, rendering social services or financial acumen we'll be willing to bet that you perform your function with great pride and a strong desire to create the very best you can. You keep up to date with the latest developments – competitive, technological, social, political and more. You understand market drivers, climate and customer needs. You present your products and services by leveraging their positive aspects. And you focus on continuous improvement. Certainly not on failure. And so too it should be with safety. It's time for safety heroes, not safety zeroes. As the late legendary boxer Muhammed Ali remarked *"Don't count the days, make the days count."*

Creating safety is a concept introduced by Andrew in his book on safety culture entitled *From Accidents to Zero*. If you've read that book you'll know already that at the heart of the idea is the idea of asking great questions. We both believe that being a great leader is not necessarily about having all the right answers, but rather more about being able to ask the right questions. You can start asking yourself some right away: Do you recognize all the positive things that you and your colleagues accomplish to make safety part of the normal way of life for your organization? Do you acknowledge and celebrate all the good that others are doing in the workplace? And do you actively seek out opportunities to help them do more to make things safer?

Look, don't get us wrong: we don't mean to say that you shouldn't learn from your mistakes of course. We simply propose that you work to get the balance *just right*. Whilst you're in the process of creating safety, accidents may occur. After all, none of us are perfect. Most of us appreciate, enjoy and are motivated by the ability and opportunity to learn and grow, to mature our thinking, to build our experience. So when exploring why your accidents have happened aim to take a view from each of these three causation levels:

1 **Root Causes** – these are the characteristics or behaviours from which all others develop. They might be distant with regard to time and space from an incident or accident itself, and may be connected to how the organization is managed operationally. It's here that leaders can have significant influence in reducing the potential of root causes developing into injury because you can identify those behaviours, learn from them and put them right. Think about how you support the promotion and communication of activities, campaigns and initiatives to improve safety management within your company.

2 **Underlying Causes** – typically these are the unsafe acts or conditions that have led to an injury (or Near Miss) occurring. As a leader you may not be in the exact spot when an accident is about to occur so it's crucial that you use your influence to set the tone to establish and shape a positive safety culture within your organization. That means creating a culture where everyone knows its ok to raise concerns and people take responsibility.

3 **Direct Causes** – are as the name suggests, the actual proponents of harm causing the actual injury – for example an unguarded moving part of machinery, a hazardous chemical, and so on. Identifying the direct cause and communicating the risk to other parts of the organization is central to maximizing shared learnings.

As you become more involved in the accident investigation process there are also three contributory factors groups worth considering in more detail:

1 **Corporate Policy** factors – consider the prevailing corporate culture and how it affects safety in the workplace. Look at how safety management is owned (in terms of discharge of responsibility), controlled and delivered. Think about broader workforce dynamics such as the pressure to perform, relations with trades unions, and so on.

2 **Organizational** factors – At this level look at your company's training, instruction, supervision and instruction of staff. Think more closely around the workplace culture, how safety is communicated, received and perceived. Consider whether organizational processes including procurement, quality control, maintenance, process design and engineering, and relationships with contract labour may affect safety.

3 **Direct** factors – Here it's all about your people. How is morale and motivation? Do workers have the skill, knowledge and competence to perform their tasks safely? What access do workers have to good information on safety and workplace risk – is it limited to a dusty old manual somewhere, a safety noticeboard, or is there a regular, effective mix of verbal and non-verbal communications in place to ensure they are kept appraised? Look broadly at worker health, fatigue, rest and rehabilitation. How is their risk perception and situational awareness? Look at the equipment involved, the workplace conditions generally, and the safety features such as emergency stop buttons, alarm systems, barriers and guarding.

What you may notice in this list of factors is that words like culture, people and human factors feature strongly. You should also spot that there is a strong sense of finding out, learning and putting things right. It is <u>not</u> about seeking out who can be blamed. Safety really is about managing and leading people much more than it is about systems. We will expand on this point in more detail in the following chapters but for now just bear in mind that managing and leading safety is about creating a culture that's *just right*. It cannot be achieved in a few weeks or a few months. It takes time and there may be setbacks along the way but it is essential to achieving something which is successful and just as importantly, sustainable.

From rose-tinted glasses to the future

We know that you've picked up this book and are reading it because you're a realist. You see things as they are. And you hope that we'll be looking from a similar angle to you. If you are starting out on this journey, we need to acknowledge that for a while yet, accidents may indeed happen at your place of work. Some of them may even be very serious, but we have faith in you and how you'll handle them. But as we move forward, let's build a vision of a world where everyone goes home from work without harm. Everyone. Every day. Let's not get caught wearing rose-tinted spectacles naively regarding those Accident Frequency Rate charts as confidence-boosters, but instead maintain a duality of perspective: one that sees what the situation currently is and fully explores and understands the reasons for our failures in safety, while at the same time seeing what could be possible, learning from the mistakes and taking positive action towards achieving our new goals. If we can grasp this new mindset, great things are possible.

It's almost time for us now to face the future and work out what these *great things* are and how to achieve them. But before we move onward, let's just reconsider the key points from this chapter and reflect on where you are right now.

1 Take a wander around your workplace. With an objective eye, what's your take on safety signage and the use of personal protective equipment? Have your workers become sign-blind, or do you think the balance is *just right*?

2 Consider your own personal experience as a leader – have you felt a difference between the *Real World* and the *Paper World* of safety? What has caused this feeling? How might you align the two worlds more closely?

3 How is safety data received and interpreted by your organization's senior leadership team? Your peers may not need to understand exactly how data is calculated but they would be prudent to know what it means. How does the team respond to the data? And how does the data inform and shape the activities you do to improve safety in the workplace?

4 Even if safety is first on the agenda at your board meetings, look beyond the obvious and consider the quality of the conversation which takes place.

5 What cultural clues can you spot that illuminate the beliefs and values of your work groups and teams? How do cultures differ across your organizations footprint? And what are the commonalities that unites these cultures and groups?

6 Who owns safety in your organization? The H&S Department, or you as the leader? Do your safety specialists work for and with you, to your shared agreed agenda or are they setting the pace? How integral do

you see safety to the success of your organization? Do you work to create safety or is it seen an add-on cost of doing business?

7 Finally, what do you *see* when you *look* for safety in the workplace? Do you have a natural bias to spotting hazards and failings, or are you truly recognizing great performance and contribution? There's a balance to be had here isn't there? Do you feel that you have it *just right*?

Footnotes

1 Inattentional blindness is a fascinating concept, you can read more about it in Andrew's book *From Accidents to Zero*, find out more at www.fromaccidentstozero.com

2 In the UK this is what's known as being 'reasonably practicable'.

3 Two excellent explorations of culture are contained in: Hofstede, G. (2001) *Culture's Consequences: Comparing Values, Behaviors, Institutions and Organizations Across Nations*, 2nd Edition. And also Hofstede, G., Hofstede, G.J. and Minkov, M. (2010) *Cultures and Organizations: Software of the Mind*. 3rd Edition.

4 Heinrich, H.W. (1951) *Industrial Accident Prevention*, 3rd Edition.

5 Heinrich was not the only one to consider the relationships between different levels of accidents. His famous 'Triangle Model' was replicated by Frank Bird in the 1970s, and further by several regulatory agencies – including the UK Health & Safety Executive – academic institutions, and research bodies over the years. Whilst different numbers have been presented by each successive author – causing much debate amongst the safety profession – the principle of a relationship between the accident types is generally sound and one which we both support.

6 Without doubt there is learning to be gained from looking at Near Misses in the workplace and the application of corrective measures to reduce the chance of a more serious accident. There is, as you might expect, no predicting when each of the various types of accident will occur but whilst resolving Near Misses may not in itself eliminate major accidents, it will – if approached *just right* help develop a positive and systematic method to workplace safety that reduces their likelihood.

You don't learn to walk by following rules. You learn by doing, and by falling over. The rules don't guarantee success, because there is no recipe for success.

There's so much more to be gained from not knowing how to do things the 'correct' way, and learning to do them your own way. So forget the rules and learn from first-hand experience instead.

Richard Branson, Entrepreneur & Founder of the Virgin Group

CHAPTER 4
Facing the Future

In the previous chapter we explored some of the pitfalls common to organizations today when it comes to workplace safety. We also introduced the concept of *creating safety* and suggested that it's time to re-position your mindset over matter.

So the question is, how can we build a different paradigm?

Well we have no doubt that if you've read this far in this book, that at least some progress has already been made in breaking out of the cycle – and the talk is now all about leadership. But leadership by whom and of what, exactly? We've established that our focus is not about kids playing conkers, baskets of flowers falling on our heads, and creating copious amounts of paperwork. Rather, the purpose of workplace health and safety is to ensure that all of our employees are able to do their job well and go home to their families without harm every day. And then return tomorrow to do more of the same.

We have to move away from the very real risk of those over-burdened or over-zealous practitioners creating more and more checklists and driving organizations to the brink of self-destruction with their bureaucracy[1]. We also need to tackle insurers who advise you to take steps to reduce risks that seem trivial to you without a sensible discussion about whether or not you are willing to bear that risk. And we must also challenge those lawyers who tell you that you can't share valuable knowledge and learning with others which would save lives for fear of some highly improbable lawsuit.

So it's really all about deciding for yourself how you want your business to be run and what sort of reputation you want to build for the business – and for yourself as a leader – with your workforce and with your stakeholders. It's about understanding and focusing on the real risks and being brave enough to say what you're not going to do because it's unimportant or bureaucratic, rather than blaming it on some health and safety regulation that simply doesn't exist.

So whose leadership are we talking about here? Well, that question is easy to answer – it's yours!

Are we there yet?

So how do you tell when your organization is in a good place? It's just like making porridge – not too little, not too much, not too hot, not too cold. It needs to be *just right*. But what's the secret? You just need to find Goldilocks and ask.

But *who* is Goldilocks? And where are they? Well the good news is, there's more than one. You'll find Goldilocks on your factory shop-floor, in your Engineering workshop, amongst your supervisors, in your management team, with your Trade Union representatives, and almost everywhere else you care to look within your business.

What to ask? Well more good news – you don't need to define a complex employee questionnaire. We've seen many questionnaires that contain the 'golden question' of *"Is health and safety important in this organization?"* and encountered many responses, here's some of them:

"Yes it is. This is the best place I've ever worked in"

"It's obvious that management really cares"

"I know someone will listen if I raise concerns"

"It's ridiculous the amount of paperwork we have to go through"

"They say it is but they don't really mean it"

"Only on the day shift: nobody cares what happens out of hours"

"It's completely over the top, we can't get the job done"

"They focus on the wrong things"

"They care about their own staff but not if you're a contractor"

By now we reckon that you will be able to assess for yourself which of these responses indicate just the right sort of culture and which ones indicate that all is not well. The key here is that it is about creating an organizational culture based on caring about *how* things are done, not putting a cover-everything-rules-based-system in place or over-bureaucratizing with audit forms, checklists and inspections.

Just so that we are totally clear and on the same page, let's look more closely at what some of the responses tell us about the culture:

"They say it but they don't really mean it"

This is an organization where there will be a lot of visible signs that safety is important – possibly in the form of signage, as we discussed in the previous chapter, but it may also come from a lack of visible management. On the surface organizations like this will demonstrate a high level of commitment to safety – probably through paperwork. But then, how does the workforce get the sense that they don't mean it? Because the actions and the messages are inconsistent – and when you look deeper, there's no real and tangible evidence of engagement with the workforce on matters of safety:

- At crunch times when the pressure is on to meet a particular deadline, safety rules and procedures which operate normally at other times will be overlooked *"just this once"*.

- Employees will be encouraged to raise safety concerns, but when they do the concern is dismissed as 'trivial' or a witch hunt ensues to find out who caused/created the problem. You will not be surprised to learn that in organizations where this happens word soon gets around that it's best to keep quiet and not raise concerns, no matter what management say.

- Rules are not enforced. The organization may have lots of rules and requirements for protective equipment, work procedures and so on but when people fail to work to the rules, the breaches are ignored and no action is taken.

- Management and supervision don't *'walk the talk'*. On management walkabouts (if they happen) people walk past someone who is taking a risk – like exceeding the site speed limit with a forklift truck or working at height unsafely – and don't follow up with the individual or their supervisor.

"Only on the day shift: nobody cares what happens out of hours"
During peak hours when everyone is around the workforce take great care to comply and supervisors will ensure that rules are adhered to, but as soon as management goes home and there are only a few people left onsite no one follows the rules.

A common catalyst of this type of organizational culture is a failure to engage first line supervisors or to train them in how to lead on safety matters. Management feels that they can tick the box because everything seems to be ok, but then the same management is often caught out when a serious incident happens out of hours when fewer people are around. In an organization like this some of the following behaviours are likely to occur:

- Management will have put in place a clear statement of the rules and expectations, and their safety policy is often proudly displayed on the Reception wall, in the canteen and coffee room, and featured on every staff noticeboard.

- Supervisors tell their teams that they must comply *'because it's the rules'* but fail to engage in discussions that build a sense of ownership of why the rules are important and should be adhered to.

- Once no one is around to monitor compliance the rules are ignored and people get on with doing the job in their own way, possibly not wearing PPE or taking time to think about the risks. You see, it's what people do when they're alone, when no-one can see them, and when they think they won't get caught that makes the difference between civilization and a jungle.

But we can't really blame the workers – they are doing what human beings do. In a top-down approach like this, usually no one has taken the time to engage with the workforce and to get them to understand what is important and why. It is often coupled with *"It's ridiculous the amount of paperwork we have to go through"*. Paperwork has become the order of the day: fill out a risk assessment for every task no matter how small; record every observation; obtain approval and a permit-to-work from several levels; and have a copy of the task safety procedure before proceeding, and so on. It's no wonder then, that on nightshift and at weekends, when the paper-mongers are safely tucked away that everything changes.

"They focus on the wrong things"
This feedback tells us that the workforce knows that there are serious risks which need to be managed but the focus of health and safety seems to be elsewhere, typically on the less important stuff.

Imagine for a moment working in a heavy industrial environment where there is lots of noise, dust and fumes. If the focus of health and safety is in the right place it will be these issues that are being tackled. But if safety walkabouts conducted by management ignore these things and instead centre on picking people up for not wearing their hard hats or spotting trailing wires on the floor the workforce will rightly say that management don't seem to know or care about the really serious risks to their health. It is worth noting at this point that focusing on safety only and ignoring or overlooking health risks is not at all uncommon. There are many good 'reasons' for this approach:

- Safety risks are more immediate: someone may hurt themselves today or tomorrow if the problem isn't fixed.

- It is more difficult to determine the cause of health problems. If an employee turns up with a sore back or a serious cough, it may not be easy to determine if this is work-related as opposed to being caused by some element of their lifestyle outside of the workplace.

- Many health risks may only manifest themselves much later in someone's life, perhaps even after they have ceased to be employed by the company. Asbestos is sadly perhaps the most common example of this, where exposure may not result in mesothelioma or other related conditions for 20-30 years. But when it does, it is, tragically, invariably fatal.

Health has traditionally been seen as 'beyond the scope' of many health and safety advisors and managers. Some practitioners have recognised the limits of their abilities and backed off from unfamiliar territories, leaving the technical medical stuff to the doctors and nurses. Recognising boundaries and limitations is all well and good, providing you actually do have someone looking at health issues for you, and those of significance are included in your general approach to managing and communicating risk – something in our experience which doesn't always happen as it should. If your health and safety practitioner is pointing out their limitations in this area, open the conversation about where you may need to go to get the expertise, whether this is an area for their personal development and explore together how you ensure health is properly addressed in the meantime. Just as we need to engage experts to help us engineer out safety risks in high hazard workplaces, some may need to engage people such as industrial hygienists and occupational physicians to engineer out exposure to conditions which harm health.

The *just right* approach to health and safety means taking account of *all* the significant risks – those that are immediate and also those that have a much longer latency period, such as risks to worker health. It is also about being prepared to tackle the most important issues even if they are difficult and the boundaries between what happens at work and at home are fuzzy.

And the *just right* approach does not differentiate between your own employees and temporary staff or contractors. They are all employed in your workplace irrespective of who pays their wages. The risks are created by the undertaking of the business so it is for you to ensure that the risks are managed – regardless of who may be exposed to the hazards. Think of the *'Newspaper Headline Test'* as we like to call it. If something significant happens from a health and safety perspective on your site would a newspaper headline point out the precise details of whose payroll the injured person was on? Or would it be your company name that would feature most prominently?

Asking others

Finding out what your people think is crucial. Charles Elvin, Chief Executive Officer of the Institute of Leadership & Management believes that:

"Good leaders listen. It's not just about telling them what you want, it's equally important that you hear what your workforce has to say and that you give them regular feedback on these things."

We know that it can be tempting to ask *someone else* for their views on whether you're doing the right thing (and why not, we all like a bit of confidence comfort) and often organizations will turn to auditors to give them the once over. When it comes to workplace safety, the OHSAS 18001 approach emanating from the British Standards Institute has been very popular in recent years. OHSAS 18001 (likely to soon to become known as ISO 45001) is an internationally recognised health and safety management system founded solidly on the *Plan, Do,*

Check, Act, Improve philosophy common to quality and environmental standards[2]. We know we don't really need to say this at this point, but whilst having a management system (even one which is audited and certified) is an important step in the right direction, it's insufficient on its own. We believe that key to creating a safe place of work is a positive, supportive organizational culture where safety is truly felt as a core value, and safe behaviour is not just 'how we work around here' but is actively recognised and reinforced by you and your leadership peers. Those auditors won't be able to tell you when it's like that, you'll find out from Goldilocks when it's *just right.*

Getting the mix *just right*

So, how do you create just the right culture? Well, first of all you must decide what you want it to look, feel, smell and taste like. It must be something that you feel comfortable presenting and talking to your staff and contractors about and it must be something you are going to stick with, and be consistent about, every single day. Just like Andrew's recipe for a great bowl of porridge!

As a leader, clearly communicating - in positive terms - what it is that you're striving for in safety, and helping people see how they can contribute to this - as individuals and in their teams, is essential. Charles Elvin at the Institute of Leadership & Management agrees:

"You need to ensure that everyone in your organization is clear about what you are trying to achieve collectively. That means setting a clear and understandable vision and, crucially, telling everyone what it is."

Talk the talk…

Here's a case in point. Recently Andrew was asked to chair an annual safety conference for a client organization. Heerema Marine Contractors ('HMC') is a world leading marine contractor in the international offshore oil and gas industry. Founded in 1948, HMC excels at transporting, installing and removing offshore facilities including fixed and floating structures, subsea pipelines and infrastructures in shallow waters, deep and ultra-deep waters. If it sounds like a tough environment, it really is. And what makes it even more impressive is that Heerema manages the entire supply chain of offshore construction from design right through to completion.

Jan-Pieter Klaver is the CEO of HMC, and when it comes to safety, he's all about leading from the front. Recognizing the importance of setting the tone, Klaver's opening address to the conference – of HMC senior leaders and contractor partners from up and down their supply chain – was pragmatic, honest, and *just right*:

"In a time where oil prices hover around $50 a barrel, and our clients are calling for cost reduction, it might be tempting to cut costs in our safety budgets. But let me explain what we do instead. Over the years we have invested in the health of our people and continue to find ways to keep them healthy and in safety we strive for a workplace that's incident and injury free."

"All of our people are trained and most of our contractors have now gone through similar programs. We focus on the hearts and minds of people as we believe that our people are the ones that can influence safe execution. Our people are the last in a row of safety barriers that can turn difficult situations into manageable solutions. Key here is that we care, and that we give our people a mandate to stop the job if they don't feel safe. Care works if the company is consistent in its message and creates the right culture. I

am personally very proud to work with a workforce that is enthusiastic and committed to safety."

"It is time now to go back to basics. In safety we enjoy positive discussions with our clients to adjust our focus back to the work floor (and away from dollar price). That means less paper work, less policing from the clients often hired-in inspectors. More focus on working with contractors safety management systems, a more integrated approach, and encouraging a proactive culture where we plan the work and work the plan."

Klaver's address is backed up with substance and pride. He looks each attendee at the conference in the eye as he speaks. You can palpably feel that this man *cares*. He sees the future success of his business and the ongoing health and prosperity of his people as interconnected. And they know it too. Talking with HMC installation managers and supervisors, and with contractor organizations over lunch each is in no doubt about the worth of Klaver's message. They're quick to explain that it's *"not negotiable"* yet it feels not like an edict but rather more *"like the guiding hand and caring words of a parent"* as one explains.

…And walk the talk

In a previous chapter we mentioned one manager who decided he could not bear to experience another serious safety event again. That was not an isolated case. We know of others who hold the mantra of 'Not on my watch' very much to heart.

Paul's deeply personal experience catalysed a feeling so deep and strong that he was not afraid to repeat his mantra to anyone and everyone – whether his own workforce, visitors to his company or to his peers. This leader had decided that he was in control of his future, and the way he went about it was certainly a great example of truly minding his own business. After attending one of our two-day safety leadership masterclasses in Johannesburg Paul decided he wanted the rest of his leadership team to enjoy the same training. Having already completed the class, it's fair to say that Andrew fully expected Paul to come in and introduce the program then leave his team to it. But not this CEO. 'Lead by example' may or may not be one of his mottos, but for the next two full days he had his diary cleared as he participated alongside his board colleagues. In the years following that fatal accident on one of his sites, this CEO built a personal mindset and a corporate culture that felt *just right* for him, his team, and his workers as he leads from the front in *creating safety* in his business.

When the United Kingdom Olympic Delivery Authority set out to transform a stretch of barren wasteland on the east side of London into the venue for the 2012 Olympic Games they talked about 'creating a legacy'. They very quickly realised that that legacy of a successful and inspiring Olympic Games would be seriously tarnished if people lost their lives during the construction phase. The leadership team of the ODA decided upfront that they needed to create a climate in which everyone took pride in achieving a safety culture where people looked out for everyone else. Their commitment and dedication to this approach never once faltered and today – even several years after the spectacle – the London Olympics stands out for many reasons but not least because it is the only Olympic venue ever built and the Games event staged without a single fatality. It was an extraordinary and outstanding achievement. And you only had to visit the Park during the construction phase to feel the power of the culture there – the sense of pride and the ownership at every level in the organization.

The Olympic project set a new standard for major projects in the Construction industry and it is encouraging to see others now taking that even further. The talk is now no longer of *reducing injuries* and *target zero* but of establishing new approaches which will bring even greater levels of safety and health protection hand in hand with productivity. The fascination with often hollow and meaningless 'zero injury' slogans is finally drawing to an end. Clearer assertions that both set the tone and clarify the vision are starting to appear all around the world. One of Africa's leading construction firms, Aveng Grinaker-LTA, has one that particularly caught our eye recently:

"Home without harm. Everyone. Every day."

Beautifully simple, strikingly inspirational, instantly memorable. Aveng, like many other forward-thinking organizations is *creating safety* and shaping the future. And they are seeing their businesses benefit on many levels as a result. We take our hats off to these leaders.

So what we would like you to think about here is that *legacy* issue: How can any business consider itself to be successful – whether financially, from a reputational perspective or otherwise – if it does not have a culture which takes care of the people who work there and leaves a positive imprint on them? It doesn't matter whether you manufacture cars or the latest technology, build oil platforms or construct Olympic venues, bake loaves of bread or grow fruit and vegetables, deliver waste and recycling services or anything else – doing it successfully whilst being a great employer must include having a good and strong safety culture. It isn't an add-on. It is, as Jan-Pieter Klaver says, *integral*. And it's all about creating the future that you want to lead.

We strongly suggest that you make your safety culture part of your business strategy. It must be a core value in how you want the business to operate – not a priority. Priorities change with time and circumstance, don't they? Putting *'Safety First'* today doesn't mean that it will remain there for tomorrow and the day after. But when safety is set as a corporate core value – and you really mean it – then it becomes a powerful motivator. When you show that you *really* care about your people – and they can feel it – then they will naturally respond positively.

Just a final thought about culture and walking the talk. There are many sectors today which are facing serious skills shortages. Put yourself in the position of any young person with a mortgage and a family. Given the choice between working for a company who openly states that they have a caring approach to safety and that it is integral to everything they do and one which is driven by deadlines and pressure and who really doesn't seem to care about its employees – which one would you choose to work for? This is about creating serious competitive advantage – not about cost. You know it makes sense.

Time to ditch the cotton wool

Creating safety is not about 'nannying' your people. Showing that you care does not mean doing their work for them or telling them absolutely everything they must do and how to do it in explicit detail. Some of the best health and safety policies we've seen talk about expecting every member of the workforce to behave responsibly and to look out for themselves and their co-workers. It's set out there as a clear expectation from the very beginning. If we start out by treating people as the responsible adults we expect them to be and, if everything that follows in your corporate culture supports that, then this is how they will behave. And to be clear, when we say *'everything that follows'* we mean that:

- The workforce is encouraged to raise concerns and when they do, these concerns will be objectively listened to and taken seriously. Not every concern has to be addressed, but at the very least if a concern is not going to be acted upon then the person who raised it deserves to know why.

- The workforce is asked for their views on proposed changes to work and input to safety procedures and risk assessments. When a procedure or risk assessment is developed in this way, it will reflect how the job is *actually* done and will take account of possible shortcuts people might take. Of course, if a short cut presents a significant risk then the reasons for not doing that particular practice need to be properly explained.

- We don't want to try to state the blindingly obvious here, but focusing on the things that really matter, really matters. But how do you know what these are? Well more of that later in this chapter, but taking a helicopter view, in a mature organization it means that the things that are important will not have been determined only by a select few at the very top of the organization or in the health and safety manager's office but rather by a consensus-building process where the views and perspectives of the workforce are considered. When was the last time you asked your people what really matters to them? Did safety feature in their replies? We'd be surprised if it didn't – unless of course you're already making great porridge.

Creating a positive culture around safety feels good. You are the leader, but the responsibility and ownership is shared amongst everyone in the workplace. Yes, we know that 'shared responsibility' might sound a bit fuzzy, but really it isn't. It just means being clear about everyone's specific responsibilities. Or as Judith so succinctly heard someone put it recently *"Everyone knows the three or four things that they must do to be part of making the whole system a success."*

Back to the future

When Judith went to work for Exxon at their Fawley plant in the United Kingdom, back in 1975 it was an exciting place to be a young engineer. Exciting because of its complexity, because of the strong work ethic but also because everyone clearly recognised there was a serious responsibility to do what they were doing *safely*. As with any major hazard industry, such invention and industrialisation cannot take place effectively, if at all, without identifying, understanding and managing the risks inherent in the processes and in any changes or modifications that might need to be made for any new process.

Judith recognises that she was trained well in her early career. As she drove onto site each day she was met by that large sign we mentioned earlier painted on the side of an oil storage tank which advised everyone who entered through that gate that:

"<u>You</u> are responsible for safety on this site."

But it was about much more than slogans and signs. Safety truly was embedded in every facet of everyone's role on the site. Here's an illustration briefly describing how change management was handled – and don't forget, this is a process that was in place back in the 1970s. As a process engineer, it was Judith's job to come up with ways to improve the plant – to use less energy, to improve yields or to make new products. Her boss would encourage her to come up with new good ideas – and to seek out more from plant operators, engineers and technicians. It was abundantly clear to her that not only did she need to come forward with a way of doing things better, but a way of doing things better *safely*.

Having persuaded her immediate supervisor that a new idea was sound,

Judith then had to convince others, including the operators of the plant and those who would maintain it as well as more senior management. Only after all this would the change be put into play and only then if it was a relatively small change. For larger scale changes and capital projects this process was then followed by a review by a group of senior engineers and managers called the *'Safe Operations Committee'*. Let's be clear here, this was not bureaucracy, this was proper old-school face-to-face discussion. It was a challenging process for the young engineer – and it was *meant to be*. Only when everyone was happy that the change could be implemented, and implemented *safely*, did it go ahead.

As her career progressed and Judith became an Operations Manager, she also became a member of that very same 'Safe Operations Committee', reviewing and challenging the good ideas of others. Her role was now different, but it was nonetheless clear what her responsibility was. And the core value of the corporation also remained strongly the same.

The key point from these days of early career development and training was that managing risk and ensuring safety was an *integral part* of every role Judith was appointed to – her responsibilities were clear and so were everyone else's, and they all understood that. Looking back over those decades there is no doubt that the golden thread of safety that started at the factory gates in Fawley continues to be woven ever-stronger through Judith's career to the present day.

It's not *my* job

You may be asking yourselves *"But what about those people who just seem like they don't want to take responsibility?"* Well it's right here that your leadership becomes critical.

We have seen too many organizations where the culture is built upon the lowest common denominator. Their porridge is either too hot – those organizations that feel that they must cover everything *'in case someone does something really stupid'* or it's too cold – where the lowest safety standard set by the leaders is the highest standard the workers will aspire to and attain.

If your desired *just right* culture is one of people taking responsibility, then this lowest common denominator approach simply won't work (but it will generate a *lot* of paperwork). Instead you must be prepared to:

- Make safety explicit in job roles and responsibilities

- Provide information and training in what this means

- Monitor, measure and provide feedback on workplace behaviour

- Deal properly with individuals who flout the rules, using your organization's disciplinary process where the breach of rules is serious

If the culture you create is one that the vast majority of the workforce like and buy into, you may not have to deal with too many outliers partly because their peers will already have discouraged them from their reluctance, negative attitudes or bad behaviours. They will be looking out for each other and they will not want to risk the culture which they like being spoiled by a few who behave irresponsibly.

Peer pressure is a powerful thing indeed and if you can create a collectively owned and shared approach, the outliers will find it much more difficult than if the system is one of bureaucracy and policing by those from the top, when they are around – because everyone feels stifled by this type of approach.

There's a classic experiment that underlines the importance of peer pressure and its effect on culture, and on group and individual behaviour. So just to give us an interesting illustration – away from usual domain of safety – let's share it here. It's an example to illustrate how culture spreads but please beware we are not advocating creating culture without explaining why certain behaviours are important. That said, let's have a look.

A cage contains five monkeys, at the top of the cage a banana is hung from a string, and a set of steps is positioned beneath the banana. Fairly quickly, the monkeys will notice the banana and one will go to the steps and climb up. As soon as he touches the steps, all of the other monkeys are sprayed with cold water.

A short while later, another monkey dares to make the same attempt to get the banana. As soon as he reaches the steps, all of the other monkeys in the cage are sprayed with cold water. You can imagine, they're not happy chimps.

At this point one monkey is removed from the cage and replaced with a new monkey. It doesn't take long before he notices the banana and makes a start for the steps. To his surprise though, before he reaches the steps, he is attacked by his peers and prevented from reaching the banana. After another attempt is met with the same response from the other monkeys, he understands that if he tries to reach the banana he'll be assaulted by the others, so he joins them on the other side of the cage, away from the treat.

Now another of those original monkeys is removed from the cage and replaced with a new monkey. As he enters, he notices the banana and makes for the steps. Just like before, he's instantly set upon by the other monkeys – including the recent newcomer. The experiment continues, with a third original monkey being replaced by a new one. He gets to the steps and is set upon by the group – however this time, two of the four monkeys taking part in the punishment have no idea why they weren't previously permitted to climb the steps and take the banana and also no idea why they are beating this new monkey.

The trial progresses, replacing the fourth and fifth original monkeys with new ones. Now all of those original monkeys that were sprayed with cold water have gone, but despite this, none of the current five ever approach the steps – even though they want the banana. Why not? Because as far as the monkeys are all aware, this is the way it's always been around here.

Assessing the risks and keeping it real

Building a culture of safety that's *just right* means efficiently and effectively managing the risks in your workplace. Often the term 'risk assessment' is given interchangeably to any and all documents that claims to demonstrate good management of health and safety risks for a particular activity. But this isn't quite correct. Risk assessment and risk management is, as the full title suggests, a *process*. Any output from this process – whether in the form of a Risk Assessment, a Method Statement or any other document claiming to 'manage safety' should include the following core elements:

- A clear and concise description of the activity to which it relates

- Identification of the hazards associated with the task or activity

- Details on who undertakes the activity (not their names, role titles will usually suffice), where and when, and what competencies, special skills, resources and equipment are needed

- An evaluation of the risks likely to arise during the activity, together with the necessary control measures to be taken to mitigate these risks

We've already talked about the need for risk assessment and risk management to be integrated and within a constant state of mind in the workplace, just as it is (or at least should be) for all of us in living our lives. In the workplace lots of tasks are routine and will be carried out by a range of people across different shift patterns, so it makes sense to do one risk assessment and for that then to lead to risk management measures which everyone is aware of. Ah, we hear you say, but not everyone is the same – some people are more likely to put themselves at risk than others. That's very true but a decent risk assessment will consider those <u>most</u> at risk – be they for example new and inexperienced employees, pregnant workers, or those with particular needs – as well as those who are so familiar with the job that they've stopped seeing the risks.

Generic risk assessments like these don't need to keep being repeated. We've seen many organizations that believe they need to repeat the assessment every couple of months. They do need to be reviewed from time to time though – but only to check if there have been any significant changes which affect the risk. Oh, and it's always a good idea to review the risk assessment in the aftermath of an accident or near miss to explore how you might tighten things up a little more in order to prevent a recurrence.

Who can conduct a risk assessment? Well, for a start, *you* can. But why try to do it on your own? The best person to ask to support you is the individual engaged in the activity: they're well placed to understand the nuances and detail of the task, and will almost certainly know the risks. Invite your safety manager and – if you have one in your workplace – your Trade Union safety representative to the team. They'll each bring different perspectives, perhaps an understanding of any specific legal requirements you'll need to be mindful of, and some further technical skills too. Recall our earlier advice though and never be afraid to challenge the source of the advice you receive – from anyone – if it sounds over the top.

We're going to suggest something really old-fashioned here – do the risk assessment out on the job, actually looking at the task. There's been a tendency for some safety experts and operational managers to be happy talking about risks amongst each other in a meeting room at the opposite end of the hallway from the shop-floor. Get your assessment team out there where the action is, get the conversation flowing to identify and agree the key risks and how they should he handled. Record the key points of the conversation. It doesn't have to be a long checklist marked 'Risk Assessment' to be effective – a record of the discussion on what is agreed and the control measures to be taken is what matters. And don't fall into the trap that *"it's not a proper risk assessment unless it's on a specific form"*. There are many good online templates that can be used and almost all of the regulatory bodies, charitable institutions and membership bodies in the world of workplace safety *(see for example our notes on IOSH, IIRSM, British Safety Council, SAIOSH, ASSE and more)* have something on the web that you'll find useful.

Once you've got the assessment done, it's time to take action. Remember the risk assessment is not an end in itself – it is the first step which has then to be followed by good risk management and control. You don't need to eliminate all risks (unless of course the risk is so great that it's likely to cause massive destruction immediately). Health and safety laws around the globe call for the same thing: effective risk management. In practice this means reducing the risk to a reasonable and an acceptable level. But yes, we hear you cry *"Acceptable to whom?"* This is where the act of conversation really helps because you can agree with experts and with the person doing the job what makes sense. Those experts can advise you on international standards, specific laws and industry best practices. The workers can tell you what is practical, and if you ask the right questions they will tell you if control measures are over the top and likely to lead to creative workaround by them and their colleagues.

When considering implementation of control measures to reduce the risks, there are five key principles that will serve you well. A combination of these may be possible, but it's also worth seeing the list as a hierarchy of controls – starting from the top and working your way down:

1 **Eliminate or reduce the hazards**. What practical measures can be taken to reduce the risk of injury? The key word here is *practical* – there might be some things that are simply technically impossible or would cause an imbalance in cost versus benefit.

2 **Isolate hazards at source**. Finding ways to separate or create distance between the hazard and your employees eliminates or reduces the risk. Consult your engineers here – there may be some controls that they can introduce to reduce the risk of injuries occurring. Make sure any engineering controls can't be easily over-ridden.

3 **Minimise risk through systems and design**. Devise a way of doing the job that reduces or eliminates the risk or specify the way in which the job must be done to minimise risk. Remember, this will require careful communication to ensure that people understand why the job must be done this way.

4 **Personal protective measures**. Notice how far down the hierarchy hard hats and hi-viz vests come. Don't be tempted to promote this one above others, PPE is always supplementary to the other controls you adopt.

5 **Behavioural and administrative controls**. Minimising exposure to risk through job rotation and shift patterns sits here, at the end of the list. Rarely sufficient on their own (even in the most mature organizations we've seen this one fail – see the sections above on BP and DuPont if you need a reminder why these won't work in isolation).

How you record and communicate the risk assessment and the control measures is crucial. It makes the difference between adding value and wasting time. The key here is to do what is practical and what will get used. Risk assessments are not documents which sit on shelves in the manager's office to show to inspectors or insurers who ask to see them – they are a means of communicating with your workforce how to do the job properly and must be in a format that is friendly and accessible for the people who really need to see and understand them.

With today's technology the ways of recording and communicating risk assessments are almost limitless. Judith recently came across a brilliant tool being used by a major retail chain in the UK: the right way of doing many routine tasks has been recorded on video and the short film clips are shared with the whole supervisory team throughout the country at every branch. All the supervisors have iPads or other tablets and are able to show members of their team the right way of doing a task, right there on the job in a matter of seconds. We told you this love affair with paperwork was boring. Grab the technology and jump into the 21st century!

The best approaches to risk assessment and control are those that are integral to the job. In many high hazard industries, utilities, manufacturing and heavy engineering sectors this manifests itself in the form of a permit to work. When equipment is handed over from the usual operators to those who carry out maintenance work the permit will describe the work to be done. It will encourage the responsible person to consider how the equipment is to be isolated and made safe before being worked on. It also prompts people to consider whether additional safety protection measures are required – ranging from protective clothing to emergency arrangements. The plant or equipment is then formally handed over for the work to be done and the permit is 'live'.

When the work is complete the maintenance person hands the paperwork back to the operator stating that the work is done. The operator will then check the status of the work and should only sign it off as complete when he is satisfied that it is safe to do so and that it's safe to start back up again. We want to be clear here that this is risk assessment and management in action. There is no need for separate risk assessment paperwork when it is integrated into the job like this.

Let's take a look again at another sector we mentioned earlier where the same principle applies: the world of residential or respite care. Care workers looking after the elderly and vulnerable produce Care Plans. These documents consider what the residents can and cannot be given to eat and drink, what their physical and mental capabilities are, and what help and assistance they require. It will consider whether they can handle stairs on their own, whether they need to be lifted into and out of their chairs, the bath and so on. They will also consider the risks to the carers themselves in carrying out their work. These Care Plans are a risk assessment and management plan all in one – even if the industry calls them Care Plans. Just like in our previous example there is simply no need for a separate piece of paper called a 'risk assessment'. Here again the risk assessment and management process is *integral* to the way in which work is organised and communicated.

Mindfully integrate

We've said many times in this book that being mindful of risk and taking steps to manage it needs to be an integral part of what everyone does all of the time. If you've got to this point in the book, we feel sure that the key question for you now as the leader may well be:

"How do I create an environment where people actually want to do that?"

The answer is that you need to make it easy and straightforward to do – you build it into doing the job – and you don't need to create a separate system of paperwork and bureaucracy which gets in the way.

Creating just the right culture and making safety part of the job has to be handled in a way that fits into your work environment. We know of many workplaces where this takes the form of a very short briefing every morning in the locker room or the tea shack, led by the foreman or supervisor, it is a quick discussion about the jobs to be done today, the hazards that need to be considered – including factors like the weather if the work is outdoors. It's a team talk led by the supervisor and communicated in a way that he or she knows will resonate with his or her team. It creates an opportunity for people to raise concerns if they have any. It's dynamic, it's current, it's real. But above all else it's simple and straightforward. And that's why we like it.

But this is just a suggestion, right? Your job as the leader is to decide if this is an appropriate tool for your workplace and your team. When you see or hear good ideas that are working for other people, pick them up and consider them, and implement them if they feel right. We often talk about the need for safety measures to be proportionate to the risk but equally they need to be appropriate for the culture and the nature of the workforce. If you're not sure, ask. The very action of your building a conversation around workplace safety will do wonders, we promise.

Proportionately investigate

We mentioned in the previous chapter that embarking on this journey to creating and embedding safety will take time – and consistent effort. We can't guarantee that along the way there won't be incidents that will cause you to stop and think. Heaven forbid, but someone in your workplace may even get hurt. How you react when things go wrong is a key part of being an effective leader. First of all, consider when an incident really is a failure of the system in your workplace. We've seen incident investigations launched when someone has been stung by a wasp in the office or when someone has received a paper cut whilst compiling documents at the photocopier. Both have resulted in significant accident investigation reports circulated to entire management populations and cross-company alerts to be read to all employees.

It really is for you to decide if such action is appropriate but we would urge you to ensure that any reaction is proportionate. The paper cut is not really a safety incident and the wasp sting is only a concern in as much as you may need to be sure that you know who in your workforce may be allergic to wasp stings so that if it happens to them the action taken responds to their particular vulnerability. In contrast we've also seen serious injuries where people have ended up in hospital and the corrective action list stops short with advice that workers should 'be more careful'.

Following most major incidents many corporate leaders and safety experts in that organization and more broadly, attest that they 'want to learn' about what happened, but this is often coupled with a (perhaps more pressing) underlying need to find a particular quirk or practice which existed in that unfortunate organization that makes it different from their own – and therefore enables a quick and often fallacious conclusion that what happened there 'couldn't happen here'. We think that more businesses today need to create a culture of safety where there is a real and honest desire to learn from others, to seek out examples of good practice and to shamelessly copy them.

Bear in mind that the primary purpose of investigating any incident is to understand what happened and learn lessons which help prevent a recurrence. Before the Costa Concordia ferry sprung a leak, so too did the Herald of Free Enterprise at Zeebrugge. A decade before BP's Deepwater Horizon rig burst into flames killing 11 people, their Texas City plant erupted into a fireball. Sure these are the headline-hitters, but time and time again we hear organizational leaders cry *"How have we managed to have another accident like this?"* In fact, just very recently the CEO of a multinational construction firm lamented to Andrew that *"We've managed to eliminate most serious accidents from our sites now, with the exception of falls from height. We still have one of those almost exactly every two months. And often they're quite serious."* We suspect there is something to be explored here in terms of identifying the real root causes.

When you do decide to investigate an incident make sure you have the right people on the team – again we strongly advocate involving at least someone from the workforce, they're simply closer to the action and have a different, often clearer perspective. Take time to understand what exactly was going on at the time – did the person involved feel under pressure? Was he or she distracted? If they did not follow the correct procedures why was that the case – is the current procedure impractical? The key questions are about what went wrong, why they went wrong and what can be learned. The purpose of investigations is to learn lessons and put things right, not to find someone to pin the blame on. Those days have long gone.

We're not saying there won't be times when incidents occur because someone has done something which they shouldn't have done. But if you ask the right questions this will come out during the course of the investigation and with skill you will also find out why they made that poor decision. Word soon gets around in any organization where 'accident investigation' really means 'worker witch-hunt' – and in these organizations getting to the truth and learning important lessons becomes virtually impossible because everyone clams up. Your approach to investigations, just like everything else is a very important message about the culture you're creating.

Root Cause Analysis – going to *Gemba*

A practical and popular way to get to the root cause of accidents is to us what's known as the 'Five Why' technique. Talichi Ohno, former Toyota engineer and pioneer of the Toyota Production System first created the technique as a way to solve quality problems in the 1950s. According to Ohno *"Having no problems is the biggest problem of all."* This positivist approach considers problems not as negative but rather as continuous improvement opportunities in disguise. Whenever an issue arose he would encourage his staff to get out onto the shop floor and explore problems first-hand until they could identify the root cause and resolve it. Ohno would advise his team to *"Observe the production floor without preconceptions. Ask 'why?' five times about every matter."*

A classic example of the 'Five Why' technique in action, oft-cited by Ohno, is applied to the case of an automated welding machine stopping mid-operation. Demonstrating the utility and efficacy of his method, Ohno would persistently ask why until finally identifying the root cause of the problem, here's a transcript:

Q: **"Why did the welding machine stop?"**
A: The electrical circuit was overloaded, and this caused a fuse to blow.

Q: **"Why was the circuit overloaded?"**
A: There was insufficient lubrication on the bearings, so they locked up.

Q: **"Why was there insufficient lubrication on the bearings?"**
A: The oil pump on the machine is not circulating sufficient oil.

Q: **"Why is the pump not circulating sufficient oil?"**
A: The pump intake is clogged with metal shavings.

Q: **"Why is the intake clogged with metal shavings?"**
A: Because there is no filter on the pump.

In five steps we progress steadily from the initial failure of the machine to clarity on the potential root cause. Bear in mind when searching for a root cause that you are looking to identify the most basic cause that can be found and fixed. *"The root cause of any problem is the key to a lasting solution"* Ohno was known to say. He advocated and emphasized the importance of *genchi genbutsu* – roughly translated as 'going to the source' – and clarifying the problem with one's own eyes. Today, especially in organizations which support lean manufacturing and Six Sigma processes, this is known as *'going to gemba'*. Before actually getting out there to gemba, though, here's some thoughts to get your mind straight:

1 Before you begin, consider how to get the best out of the answers you receive to your Five Whys. For simple accidents you may feel comfortable doing this on your own, however for more complex or technical events it may be prudent to create a small team which includes specialists from engineering, safety and other functions.

2 Remember that the purpose of the Five Why process is to gather evidence. Keep an open, objective mind and clearly distinguish between facts and opinions.

3 Begin with clarity of what actually happened. Creating a brief definition statement may help you and those to whom you ask questions. The statement might be something like *"The injured person was conducting routine maintenance on the cardboard box packaging line 4 at 12.35pm on 6th June. The right sleeve of his overalls was caught on the moving discharge conveyor belt (plant ID #621) and he was pulled into the machine suffering lacerations and broken bones to his right arm and severe bruising to his face and right shoulder."*

4 With the definition statement in place it's time to start asking 'Why?'. Be sure to write down the answers to each question – you could use a flowchart or decision-tree type diagram to help show the cascade of questions and answers.

5 Each answer you receive in turn should reveal further fact or evidence. Where you feel that clear evidence is not provided, don't dismiss the answer until you have had chance to confirm what you are receiving.

6 Repeat your 'Why?' question until you arrive at a clear root cause. You may find that some tiers of the process generate more than one answer, and in these cases your Five Why process may broaden into a couple of tracks running simultaneously. Don't despair, follow each to

their logical conclusion and bear in mind that five is just a suggested number of times to ask why – you may need more (or less) questions in some circumstances.

The Five Why technique is a useful way to help identify the root causes of accidents in the workplace in order to put controls in place to prevent a recurrence. When conducted well it can add great value to the accident investigation process and make a positive contribution to the way in which your organization manages workplace risks. In other words, it leads you to tangible problems which can be fixed once and for all rather than the all too often 'try harder' or 'take more care' weak recommendations.

Bear in mind that accidents go beyond the work plant, equipment and processes and also have a softer, human side too. The 'ripple effect' following an accident can often reach far and wide. For example, co-workers of those involved in a workplace accident may become upset or traumatized by an injury to one of their colleagues. In the event of a very serious accident it is often worthwhile considering the provision of a counselling support service – typically an onsite specialist advisor who is there for employees to talk through how they are feeling. Managed sensitively, this can often build a sense of care and trust, and many organizations we know have found that with such support post-accident employees feel more confident to come forward and suggest other ways to manage risk, boosting not just morale but also responsibility for creating a safer workplace.

Repositioning the role of the safety professional

We hope that if you have read this far you will be beginning to understand the importance of your role in leading on safety in order to create a culture of safety that's *just right*. We cannot stress enough that without that leadership from you it simply won't happen. That may feel a bit overwhelming, but the good news is that you are not alone. The trick is to seek out those who can help and support you in creating the culture you want to create in your business.

We've already said that copying good ideas from others is not only legitimate, it makes good business sense – so long as the idea fits with your organizational culture and processes, it may need some tweaking. There is no point in starting from scratch for the sake of it if you see others elsewhere in your own organization or in a similar company doing something that you think would translate and work well in your business. And given the mobility of workforces in some industry sectors there is a good deal to be said for greater uniformity of approach rather than being different for the sake of it.

If you are a business manager no one expects you to be a health and safety expert, but we do expect you to *lead* on health and safety. If you as a leader don't think it's important, it certainly won't be important to anyone else. You are the one who can determine that keeping your workforce safe and healthy is integral to achieving productivity, maintaining motivation and continuity, fostering innovation and encouraging exceptional customer service. You don't have to do it on your own though – any more than you have to be your own accountant, HR manager, salesman or marketeer. Having decided that you want to create just the right sort of culture of safety you then call upon the experts to work with you to help you put that in place. What is key here is that they work with you in delivering the culture you want in a way that supports the business.

All too often we see health and safety professionals struggling to be heard in companies because they are not properly engaged as part of the business. They can be either literally devolved from the business, generating a world of their own, or exiled to an office at the far end of site, tucked away from 'interfering' with production. Their attendance at and contribution to board meetings is limited to a three minute stand up show and tell featuring the latest LTI (Lost Time Injury) charts – or as we referred to them earlier 'LGI charts' or 'Looking Good Indexes'. We've already covered the negative stigma surrounding safety practitioners and their profession and explored some of the reasons why they've been tarred so heavily by the media. But as a leader with a conscience – and now with a clearer understanding of your role in safety you are now in a different place and it's just possible that you may be able to strike a good deal with your H&S manager, or someone else out there in the marketplace. Be clear that you are looking for someone to help and support you create the culture *you* want to create: you don't want them to do it *for* you. You'll help them to learn more about some of the business imperatives whilst at the same time you'll seek their help to learn about some of the ways and means of implementing effective health and safety for business success. It's the win-win that's almost too easy to be true. Go on, give it a shot – the good ones will be delighted to be invited to be part of the team rather than banging the drum on the side-lines.

And so in closing…

In this chapter we've oriented you towards facing the future. This means knowing where you are now, where you want to head to, and how to identify potential bumps in the road. We've explored the fundamentals of risk assessment and accident investigation to make sure that you're not thrown off track on your journey.

A great way to find out where you are right now is to ask someone for an independent view. There's plenty of people willing to give you an answer, so we have also added some thoughts on how to evaluate what you hear. Finally, we continued our discussion on the role of the health and safety professional in your business. Whilst we do believe that there are many who have not really helped themselves (nor the profession) in moving forward and becoming part of the fabric of the business, we also know many that are exemplars of best practice, working to enable sustained success, super safety culture and great performance in their organizations. Yet for some of these dedicated practitioners, the problem they see is that they are being asked to do something beyond their competence – they are waiting for you to take the lead. These practitioners want to achieve success through active partnership and constant collaboration with their peers in operational leadership roles. None can work alone and be successful.

The final chapter in our story will explore how you take everything you've learned from this book and lead the way forward, but you know we can't finish without offering a few thoughts for you to reflect and take action on, so here they come.

1 Who is Goldilocks in your workplace? And when did you last talk to them about safety? What do your workers think about safety – is it all about the paperwork? Is a good game talked up but not delivered? Is safety a value or a priority – does its position on the priority list change depending on what else is happening? It's time to take a walk around site and ask a few fundamental questions to test the temperature and see what you need to focus on to get the mix *just right*.

2 What do you want your safety culture to look, feel, smell and taste like? Do your current initiatives, campaigns, communications, slogans and vision support that or work against it?

3 How will you as a leader set the tone for safety and lead from the front? What key activities will you begin today to demonstrate your personal commitment?

4 Where are the real and significant risks of harm in your workplace? Are you clear on how the risk assessment process is conducted and what happens to these assessments once completed? How are identified risks controlled?

5 When things do go wrong and an accident occurs what is your role? Next time, go to *gemba* and ask the Five Whys.

6 What's your relationship like with your health and safety manager? Is it a true partnership or a devolved responsibility? What do you need to do to increase collaboration and allow him or her to have a recognized and respected voice in the business?

Footnotes

1 As we've already pointed out, there are many excellent safety practitioners out there too, but whether the balance is *just right* at your place we're not sure. If you're keen to find a good practitioner, you might do well looking at their credentials. The Institution of Occupational Safety & Health ('IOSH') is the world's largest body for heath and safety professionals, with over 45,000 members around the world. IOSH's 'Chartered' status (with the post-nominals CMIOSH and CFIOSH – although the latter – a Chartered Fellow – is quite rare) signifies a practitioner who has worked steadily through a recognised route of training and qualification, and members are required to maintain Continuing Professional Development. You can find more information at www.iosh.co.uk. The International Institute of Risk & Safety Management is another UK-based professional body who seek to advance professional standards in accident prevention and occupational health throughout the world, providing both membership and education to practitioners. In the North Americas region, the American Society for Safety Engineers, and the Canadian Society of Safety Engineering are bodies with a similar purpose to IOSH and IIRSM, whilst the Safety Institute of Australia, the New Zealand Institute of Safety Management, and the South African Institute of Occupational Safety & Health do similar in their own jurisdictions. All strive to advance knowledge and 'professionalise the practice of health and safety at work' – have a look on the website of your preferred or local body and you'll likely find a wealth of information on practitioners and workplace safety more broadly.

2 At time of writing, OHSAS 18001 was in the process of turning into ISO 45001, an international standard in full alignment with ISO 9001 and ISO 14001.

We convince by our presence.

Walt Whitman, Poet, Essayist & Journalist

CHAPTER 5
Finding the Force and Leading the Way

Avoiding work-related accidents and injuries that cause pain and suffering is vitally important to us all – whether we are individual employees or department managers, industry leaders or even members of society at large. The way we do what we do – in teams, work groups and across functions – drives and reinforces the prevailing culture of the organization. As we've discussed previously, organizational culture describes the mix of shared values, beliefs and rituals that influence workers' attitudes and actions. It is, in simple terms *'the way we do things around here'*. We can think about safety culture in a similar way as being *'the way we do safety around here'*.

The relationship between safety culture, competent advice and safety performance is frequently researched but this mighty trifecta often misses the vital link – effective leadership. In this our final chapter we seek to draw together the key arguments of this book and help you find the force to lead safety at work in just the right way.

We'll begin by taking a step away from your organization for a moment to look at what's been happening out there in the wider world. In the last decade there has been number of serious events that have claimed lives and caused injury to workers around the world. Each has made headlines, shocked local (and often international) communities, and left workforces reeling. We believe that by briefly exploring further some of these events that we mentioned in the opening of this book we can quickly identify common ground that might just be helpful to you as a leader with an interest in safety, no matter which industry sector you work in.

The big bang in Buncefield

In 2005 an overflow of petrol from a bulk storage plant at Buncefield, England led to the ignition of a vapour cloud, creating a massive explosion that was heard and felt up to 100 miles away over in the Netherlands and also in France. The explosions generated a fire that devastated the surroundings and injured at least 43 people. The subsequent investigation found that a gauge for monitoring fuel volumes on one of the tanks had been sticking for several months and a high level switch for closing down the flow of petrol was inoperable. The bunds around the petrol tanks were inadequately designed and poorly maintained. The general approach to safety management, as well as the culture of safety at the site, were noted by investigators to be seriously lacking.

Tragedy in Texas

In that same year, over in the United States, BP's refinery in Texas City was the scene of disaster when a release of flammable liquid caused a tremendous explosion and fire that claimed the lives of fifteen people and injured 170 more. The United States Chemical Safety and Hazard

Investigation board said that whilst gas detection systems were in place, the root cause of the accident was organizational deficiencies at all levels of the corporation – including cost cutting, failure to invest, and production pressures. These collectively and cumulatively had impacted safety at the site. The report noted that a reliance on personal injury rate data had failed to provide a true picture of process safety performance and further stated that such data was not a useful indicator of health and safety culture at the plant. The report argued that various pressures within the organization had created a corporate culture where keeping the process running had become the top priority and that safety did not get the attention, resources or priority that it needed to have.

Former United States Secretary of State James Baker III led the team that that investigated the safety culture and operational management within BP's American refineries. Baker's report concluded that:

"BP did not set an appropriate tone at the top or establish appropriate goals and expectations about safety performance."

In Deepwater

Just five years later, on 20th April 2010, BP hit the headlines again when an oil rig burst into flames in the Gulf of Mexico. The Deepwater Horizon oil drilling platform suffered a series of explosions which turned it into a fireball killing eleven men – almost 10% of the total headcount on the rig at the time – and injuring many more. Just hours before the disaster, senior leaders had visited the rig to celebrate seven years without a Lost Time Injury. How could the site go from such a long period without injury to such a devastating disaster? Bear in mind that the absence of something doesn't necessarily mean the existence of something else. In other words, an absence of accidents doesn't mean the existence of safety. A report published by the Centre for Catastrophic Risk Management found situations spookily similar to those noted by US Secretary of State Baker at Texas City five years earlier when it noted that:

"BP's organizations and operating teams did not possess a functioning safety culture. Their system was not propelled towards the goal of managing maximum safety in all its manifestations but was rather geared towards a trip and fall compliance mentality rather than being focused on the big picture."

A return to Texas

Fast forward to November 15th 2014, when an unintended release of 10,500 kilograms of methyl mercaptan killed four workers at the DuPont chemical plant in LaPorte, Texas in the United States of America. Methyl mercaptan is used to produce insecticides and fungicides and as an additive to give natural gas that typical 'rotten egg' smell. During the incident the smell from the chemical release could be detected up to 40 miles away. When one worker was overcome by the chemical others went to her aid and they too succumbed to the gas. DuPont was charged with several violations under American safety legislation including a repeat violation for not adequately training employees on using the building's ventilation system and other safety procedures, including how they should respond if the ventilation system's extraction fans ceased operation.

"What we are seeing here in this incident in LaPorte is definitely a problem of safety culture in the corporation of DuPont" remarked Chairman of the U.S. Chemical Safety Board, Rafael Moure-Eraso.

Common failings and the dangerous pursuit of zero

Even with just a cursory outline, we are sure that you've already spotted similarities in each of these four cases. Buncefield, Texas City, Deepwater Horizon and LaPorte all appear to have at least two things in common. The investigation reports subsequent to each disaster point to weak safety cultures and indicate that *leadership was lacking*. A reliance on plant, process, rules and systems was simply not enough.

On at least three of the four sites featured in the outlines above they *thought* they had it right before the incident – because there had been a significant local focus on reducing accident rates. The target of 'zero accidents' was reported to be a key feature at each one too. As we've suggested earlier and we're not afraid to repeat again, the absence of accidents does not indicate the existence of safety. Those downward trending LTI (Lost Time Injury) charts often inspire over-confidence in the boardroom and breed complacency on the shopfloor. Unless lagging indicators, such as these, are utilized alongside a range of leading metrics in a balanced scorecard they can present numerous serious dangers in their own right, not only the misplaced confidence we see, but by driving a fear of failure within the workforce often leading to under-reporting of negative issues or adverse events. Could these have been factors in some of the events described on these pages? What do you think?

Illuminating the way ahead

Recently, in an airport lounge, Andrew had the good fortune to bump into a chap who worked for the United Kingdom Lighthouse Board. Over a glass of wine this delightful gent explained that his role was to visit each lighthouse to ensure that they continued to provide the service they are supposed to. Perhaps you're already thinking the same as was running through Andrew's mind – light goes on, turns around and stretches its beam of light as far as it can in all directions, light goes off. Repeat until daylight. But, being so reliably informed, we can share with you that it's way more technical than that. In additional to the standard visual light beam, a sophisticated Differential Global Positioning System created by the Lighthouse Board and installed at lighthouses up and down the country gives all year round service to ocean users by providing overlapping signal coverage up to 50 nautical miles (that's a land mile distance of 57.3 miles, or 92.6km) around the coasts of the UK and Ireland. Differential GPS was developed by the United States Department of Defence as a global resource for military use. It uses a constellation of 24 satellites continuously orbiting the earth and a network of receivers which together measure distance from each satellite and combine these measurements to calculate a vessels latitude, longitude, altitude, course and speed.

The signal is provided as a marine aid to navigation using real time GPS monitoring similar to that used in motor vehicles. What's more, the system offers users the capability of fixing their position to a 5 metre location with a 95% probability. Now, remember that this is out on the open ocean, and we reckon that you're also feeling pretty impressed by this technology. But our Lighthouse-man was keen to point out that the system isn't perfect:

"But that's okay…" he offered *"… because integrity is key. And that's my job – making sure the integrity of the system is high, in order to keep ocean users, whether they're in a canoe, yacht, fishing boat, ferry or cargo ship on the right track, in the right place, and safe."*

The parallels between the Differential GPS system and safety leadership in the workplace are many. Not least the final point around integrity.

Having both physical and emotional integrity and being able to demonstrate this by walking the talk is a key leadership skill. Business Coach Marielena Sabatier, CEO of *Inspiring Potential* advises that actions of leaders should match their words:

"Integrity earns respect, people then know that they can trust their manager and understand that they have put the company's goals above their personal ones. Emotional intelligence is also a vital quality for managers. The key to this is for managers to demonstrate self-awareness, understanding others and managing relationships. They need to deliver their messages with empathy and this in turn creates loyalty and followers."

Enlightenment and the art of leading forward

We have spent quite some time in this book exploring the things which are currently not right about the way health and safety is led and managed in many organizations. By now we hope that you are at the very least sceptical about those who tell you how difficult it all is or those who scare you into thinking it's all about mounds of paperwork to ensure that you stay out of jail. We have tried to create a new paradigm where getting health and safety right is an key part of being a good leader and of having a successful business. We don't know why MBA courses don't cover this ground as an integral part of preparing leaders to be successful – we *really* believe that they should. It's a significant gap in the essential toolkit of any leader not to be ready and able to lead on health and safety. The law is clear that you have responsibilities but more importantly your team expect it of you. If you don't step up and do it, no one else will. If someone else does try to take the lead on safety, or is delegated to do it by you, it will be clear to everyone that you don't own it and therefore they infer – rightly or wrongly – that it's not important to you. You'll recall that in a previous chapter we talked about the intelligence of the workforce and how they know instinctively whether the culture is right and authentic – or not.

We've also looked at some of the many myths around health and safety – myths about what you need to have in place, what the law requires, the false comfort of lots of paperwork. But now we want to turn to the task of exploding the biggest myth of all – the one that says you can only do health and safety if you have lots of in depth knowledge and that you have all the answers to all of the questions. (It's worth reflecting on who promulgates this myth and it's pretty clear that it is those who stand to gain from you seeing this as all too complex for you to tackle). We provided references in the last chapter to those organizations around the world who accredit health and safety experts. Don't get us wrong, this is very important stuff. Experts are vital and it is right and proper that professional bodies train people and assess their competence. But given the number of health and safety practitioners out there now – the number runs into 100s of thousands – of all shapes and sizes, keep in mind that professional membership and codes of conduct on their own may not always point you to the right people. As we aim to show in this book, it always pays to dig a little deeper to make sure you find a practitioner that's *just right* for your business – and that requires you to think about your needs, not ask them to tell you what you need!

We'll come back to this later, but for now we want to focus on you and your role. It's about your integrity as a leader. It's about *minding your own business* rather than leaving it to others. We've already said countless times that you must take the lead in workplace safety. You must decide how you want the culture to be in your organization – or, if you work in an organization which already has a strong and positive health and safety culture, the question is more one of how are you going to put your own personal stamp on things and demonstrate your leadership and commitment to the people who work with and for you.

So let's go back to that myth and turn it on its head. You really don't need to have all the answers – that's a fallacy. But you do need to know the questions to ask to get you started. It's much more about knowing the *right* questions to ask, than having all the right answers and it's about asking them in a way that is right for you and exemplifies your personal leadership. Here's a quick tip – we strongly recommend that you don't start by asking for data to be crunched, reports to be generated and stacks of paperwork on performance – that can come later, first you need to get a feel for the organization.

Start by asking yourself some questions and being really honest with your answers. Let's begin with these:

- Do I really know what the most significant health and safety risks are in this business?

- Has anyone asked me for my views on health and safety matters? Or has anyone told me what I should be doing or saying as a leader when it comes to workplace safety?

- What is the worst type of incident that could happen here?

- What do we do to make sure that doesn't happen?

- Would I know what to do if the worst were to happen?

- What would be the impact of a major safety incident on the success of the business?

- What do I sense when I walk around? Does it feel like a safe and caring workplace?

- Who owns safety in this place?

Well how did you get on? What did these questions reveal to you? This list is not exhaustive by any means but the questions and your answers to them should indicate to you that it is all about getting the feel, the sense, the smell and the taste of it.

Remember what we said, it's not about having all the answers. If your answer to any of these questions is *'I don't know'* then that's okay (for now), it simply means that it's time to find out – by asking the same question of others in the organization – and we mean *lots* of others. This is your chance to get input from as many people as possible, ideally by talking with them directly or if the workforce is in multiple locations and talking to them all is not practical it can be done through a cascade of meetings or through an employee survey. We reckon that face-to-face discussion is always best, just bear in mind that a challenge with any of the indirect routes such as a survey or cascade session is that you have to make clear that you want to know the truth, however unpalatable, not what people think you want to hear. You also have to be sure that the answers people give will get back to you directly, not be 'filtered' in any way by others in the system.

Taking tea with Talichi

Let's stick with the personal approach as the preferred route (although all of what follows can be handled indirectly, if that's the only practical way in your organization). Arrange to sit down and have tea with a group of people on the shop floor. Go to them, don't summon them to your office (you'll see why in a minute). Ask them what concerns them – if it's appropriate ask them to take you and show you the problem so that you can see for yourself and they can explain it in more detail.

Ask how you can help them to make this a safer workplace. Listen hard, but be sure to manage expectations. There is no point in promising to fix everything – it will be highly unlikely that you have the resources to do that – and in any case this is about dealing with the biggest issues, the things which have the potential to cause most harm. Don't pretend you have a magic wand, the smart ones won't believe you and the others will only be disappointed when you fail to deliver. You can't do everything, but you can commit to doing the most important things first – once you really understand what they are. Tell the people you talk to that you are in 'receive' mode: gathering information and wanting to understand. Commit to them that when you have gathered all the information together you will come back to them with your thoughts on how to move forward because you will want to know what they think. Now *that's* leadership!

When you have the views from the sharp end – from your discussion with the workforce, this is a good point at which to turn your attention to others and seek their input. Ask your boss and your peer group similar questions – it would be instructive to know what they think the biggest risks are, wouldn't it? It will also be interesting to see whether there is a common or diverging view between the workforce and your peers. Check in with your safety practitioner. And, of course, if you have a health and safety management team, committee, or steering group, you should also go ask them the same questions.

If you're really lucky the answers you get from everywhere in the organization will be consistent. That's not the end of the story though by any means – especially if the answers are consistently bad! At the very least consistency tells you that everyone sees things the same way, but there will be organizations where the view from the top is nothing like the view from the bottom – remember the points we made in the last chapter about rules being ignored or overlooked, different approaches when working out of hours, or management thinking it's all ok when it really isn't. Wherever the answers to your questions lie on the spectrum remember that this is rich and useful data which will help you to decide how to get started in making your mark and demonstrating your great leadership in safety.

Of course, you will need to understand what the law requires of you and your colleagues and you need to review the performance metrics of the organization, this is also an important part of building your knowledge and assessing the current state of the culture. But rather than getting bogged down in detail here are some more high level questions to consider asking first:

- When was the last time someone was injured at work? Was the incident investigated and what were the root causes?

- What was the response/follow up to the incident?

- Which are the most important pieces of health and safety legislation that apply to this site / industry?

- What metrics are in place for reporting unsafe situations before they lead to incidents?

- When was the last time a regulator visited the site and what was their feedback?

- What assessments (if any) have been done by our insurers and what were their recommendations?

- Do our own internal audit team look at health and safety as a matter of routine?

- Do we have any third party accreditations in health and safety? How do we follow up on their identified actions?

In every one of these cases, we would suggest that the all important follow up question is just as important as the question itself. So what is that follow-up question, you ask?

Well, the follow-up question, as we learned from our friend at Toyota, Talichi Ohno, is always a curious *"Why?"*. So for example,

- Why did the injury occur?

- Why did you decide to investigate? Why were the root causes not anticipated before the event?

- Why are our metrics only / primarily lagging ones rather than leading metrics that drive safe workplaces?

- Why was the regulator impressed / not impressed with what we are doing?

- Why are insurers making those recommendations / drawing these conclusions?

- Why is health and safety included / not considered as an integral part of internal risk auditing?

- Why is third party accreditation important? Why do we believe it adds value to the business?

We know that you're getting the picture by now. If you are going to lead on the basis of commitment to a set of principles and values, you need to understand what is driving the system and the reasons for everything that is in place. You need to be constantly asking yourself and others if what is in place makes sense and if it seems reasonable and proportionate – hence the relentless pursuit of the *"Why?"* question. Questions are great tools in your drive to improve workplace safety as they have the power to shift focus and build energy. Not only that, *great* questions also help you to stay forward-focussed on your task of creating safety.

When you've completed the data gathering part of the process we recommend taking time to reflect on what you have learned. This is also a very good time to step outside of your organization and seek the views of those who look in on your business. If you discovered that there has been a recent visit by a regulator or insurer and they have provided feedback, ask to see them and learn more from them directly. But this is also a very important time to be talking to your peers and your mentors. Ask them how they have seen things done elsewhere, especially asking about examples of good practice. Use your networks as much as possible – whether they are trade bodies, professional or personal networks. We would be surprised if you hit any roadblocks. Our experience is that the vast majority of people are always willing to learn and to share on health and safety matters – especially on an informal one to one basis – and especially if they feel that they have something positive to offer.

Remember that it is really important to consider carefully all of the ideas you pick up – mindless copying of what others in the industry do is not the way forward. You are seeking inspiration to create the culture that will work in *your* organization, building on what others have told you *may* work – but only if it's done in your way.

Seeing the big picture

Now comes the time to analyse everything that you have learned. What does all of this data tell you? Remember not to focus solely on the problems that you have heard about in your discussions with the people out there doing the work. There will be some sparkling gems in there – positive things that are already happening and working well that you can build on. But it's more than likely that you will also have identified some real opportunities – things that can be fixed reasonably easily and which will start to make a difference quickly.

Many of the business management tools which you have already learned and may well be using in other aspects of the business will work well when looking at safety culture too. Consider doing a S.W.O.T. analysis or an IMPACT grid (Easy *versus* Hard to do, Large *versus* Small impact) also consider doing a Force Field analysis (plotting things that are going on which help to build the culture you want versus things which are acting against it). Remember that you are minding safety the way you would mind any other aspect of your business, so why not use tools and techniques that work well in other areas? If your business runs a Lean or Six Sigma program and you have some experience in this area, start to consider how you might take this approach to improving safety. There will be no shortage of potential workplace health and safety projects that would benefit from a systematic approach using time-proven tools and rigorous stakeholder management. Don't get carried away just yet and start sponsoring too many Yellow Belt and Green Belt projects too soon, remember right now it's about assimilation of the data you have gathered!

Create the vision

When Paul O'Neill took over the reins as CEO of Alcoa Inc., one of the largest manufacturing companies in the United States of America, one of his first tasks was redefining the company's mission. O'Neill understood the impact of getting safety *just right*. Setting the tone from the top, O'Neill had a clear vision for workplace safety and the whole business was reorganized to place safety at its heart. Each and every operating procedure was reviewed and revised to proactively manage risk and increase the level of safety afforded to employees. Lines of communication were improved, dress codes and uniforms boosted, factory plant and equipment upgraded – all to support the new vision for safety. As you'd expect, pretty quickly safety turned into a meme that percolated through the entire organization. A safe workplace was the vision, working safely became the mission. Safety was the glue that bound everyone at Alcoa together and in time became the purest definition of what the company was and what it stood for. As a result of O'Neill's focus on safety the Alcoa business prospered – not just in terms of declining accident rates, but increased productivity and efficiency across the board until it rose to be the top performer on the Dow Jones Index.

So when you are clear on how you want things to be and you have tested that on a few key players, it is time to make this vision part of the fabric of the organization. Just like O'Neill, create a vision that clearly describes what success will look like in your organization and make sure that the safety and wellbeing of all those in it is an integral part of what you say[1].

Get on the move

Now it's time to think about the journey. How are you going to get to where you've articulated in your vision? First, please be realistic about how long it is going to take to get there. If you really want to change your organizational culture this is not an overnight fix – or even one that can be achieved in a matter of months. Real lasting culture change takes months to introduce and years to fully embed in an organization. You may of course be very fortunate and find yourself in a place where the culture is already pretty good and your job is to improve it, rather than wholesale change. But even this can be challenging – for example if your organization has done a really good job of creating a strong personal safety culture but has yet to tackle either the issues related to the integrity of the equipment and the process or has yet to address work related ill health issues. Don't worry though, as you'd expect from us by now, we have some ideas that might just help you. Let's have a look.

Golden rules

Yes, we did say *rules*. In spite of all that we have said about not creating a rules-based culture there are a few important rules[2] we want to put in place here, just to help guide you on your journey forward.

1 **Set a small number of well-designed targets.** It's all too easy to jump into creating a dashboard of KPIs to try to measure every aspect of workplace health and safety. We've been to board meetings where the poor safety manager toils through pages of charts and graphs whilst the executives stare at the floor. Choose two or three clear targets to aim for now, knowing that as you make progress you'll likely want to revise these in light of your progress. Try to resist a reliance on accident rates, keep in mind the concept of 'creating safety' and think about the inputs you can focus on and consider targets for these.

2 **Targets are important, but not the point**. Yes, it's important that no-one experiences an accident and the associated pain and broader suffering involved, but that's not the real point of what you're doing here. The point is that your employees are able to work safely,

without risk to their health and wellbeing, and return in one piece to their family to rest, recharge, have fun, and come back to work fit and strong again the next day, right? We know that measuring the performance of people presents a dilemma – without quantifiable goals it can be difficult to measure performance objectively. But at the same time, a targets-based approach will only get you so far, and too much focus on hard performance measures (like Accident Rates, or the number of Near Miss cards handed in each month) risks putting short term success above long term stability and the health of your workforce. Maintain your attention and activities on those inputs to creating safety, rather than getting hung up on preventing accidents.

3 **Build a great delivery team**. You have plenty of other things to lead on, not just safety, right? So build a team around you that understands what you're striving for. This team should be small but well-connected, represent the workforce and departmental functions in order to penetrate the entire business, optimistic in its approach, and have your complete trust. As you've been asking questions in the workforce you will have learned a lot about the people in your organization and their attitudes. There will almost certainly be some who are thinking in the same way as you do and share your views and your values – these are really important people who you definitely want on the team and they will be the ones who will help you to change the culture. It doesn't matter where they are in the organization, focus on them, share your ideas and your thinking with them – and ask them to give you honest, no-holds-barred, feedback. Oh, and you guessed it, this is the point at which your relationship with your health and safety practitioner is destined to either *make* or *break*. Get ready!

4 **Create a plan that's strong enough to get started.** There's a temptation to want to build a plan that takes you from here to there

over a period of years, typically three or five, right? Or to tie in and get into step with the broader business planning cycle. But is that *really* necessary? To ensure you get off to the best possible start, why not try setting out a short term plan that gets things up and running and quickly starts to return results and quick wins that boost morale and shows that you mean business. Keep it simple, focus on a handful of activities, don't let the metrics get out of hand. You can then re-group as a delivery team to review progress, check in on learnings made, agree new priorities and build your strategic (i.e. longer term) plan. This approach also encourages broader ownership and buy-in because people feel that their views make a difference as the plan is not cast in stone from day one.

5 **Be flexible.** Be prepared and willing to learn and make adjustments as you go. If it becomes abundantly clear that some aspects of your strategy are not working or, if as part of your own learning and development you hear about new ideas which you think should be incorporated into your approach, don't be afraid to fine tune things. The keys here are that you learn actively from experience and that you get the balance right – just like making that bowl of porridge – adjust the seasoning to get it *just right* whilst you're in the mix, but don't throw it all away and start again.

6 **Get all of the excuses off the table.** *"We've tried it like that before and it didn't work", "It doesn't usually happen like that in this industry", "It'll take too long", "Our culture isn't like that", "You're asking for the impossible", "This takes time away from making the products"…* The list goes on and on. We're sure that you can add a bunch more yourself here. But don't. Respect the rule and move forward towards your vision.

7 **No gimmicks or flavours of the month**. Think very carefully about what systems, standards, campaigns, initiatives or routines you want

to put in place. Remember what we have said. Your credibility, the integrity of the system and a successful outcome all depend upon you being consistent. If you decide to put in place a near miss reporting system to encourage people to identify and raise concerns, think about how this will be resourced – for the long term. It's no good putting someone onto the job for three or even six months – how the reporting system is managed and, action taken and feedback given needs to become an integral part of someone's role.

8 **Have patience.** Safety is not a quick-fix game and indeed it may take some time before results start to show themselves in terms of performance. Try to find ways of measuring progress and checking that things are moving in the that things are moving in the right direction, in a way that works for you, rather than relying solely on lagging indicators to tell you whether injury and accident performance data is improving.

9 **Stick with it.** Having the courage and the stamina to hold on in there and not be tempted to change tack when the road gets bumpy or when the rewards don't come rushing in is crucial. Unless you have a realistic view of how long it may take to deliver real change you may begin to doubt yourself at some point on this journey and there will always be others (usually those who didn't feel comfortable with the direction you decided to take) who will be only too willing to point out when things don't appear to be working as well as you'd hoped for. The time when this may be hardest is if an incident or an injury does occur, but if the investigation is done properly it will help you to verify whether your chosen path is making a positive difference. Remember that there are no guarantees of achieving zero incidents – it may be your goal but in the early months of changing the culture you must to be prepared for setbacks. Head down, but keep your eyes on the prize.

10 **Safety by routine beats safety by spasm, every time.** Spasmodic safety manifests as knee-jerk reaction coupled with intense focus following an accident, an over-zealous view that 'everything is important' right now, periods of hyperactivity as projects are set up and closed down shortly afterwards, an urgent fire-fighting style of leadership, vague aspirations and grandiose announcements of the change that's coming.

There is no substitute for sustained, well-disciplined, clear safety leadership no matter which workplace, corporation or industry sector you find yourself in. Use these rules and the daily habits that follow in the next section to weave safety into the DNA of how you work.

Putting safety first – the power of doing it daily

Earlier in this book we talked about the importance of establishing safety as a core value within your business. We also discussed the trap of elevating safety to being the 'number one priority' within your organization. Recall our simple argument – priorities change. When you shout *"Safety First!"* but then move off to focusing on production, quality, logistics or any other topic, then your commitment is brought into question and your credibility instantly starts to erode. Despite this general warning, there are times that we want you to put safety first. Yes, that's right, we *do* want <u>you</u> to put safety first. Every day.

How you as an individual leader handle the very first ten minutes of each workday doesn't just affect your personal mood and mindset it can also significantly influence how safe your workplace will be for the rest of the day. Now we're well aware of all those Harvard Business Review articles that provide lists of exactly what *'highly successful leaders'* apparently *'do first each day'* and we know all too well what those first few moments in the office feel like in the morning. There's always myriad things to do: an urgent call; an exceptional meeting; a sea of red emails; worker tensions; urgent correspondence; line breakdowns or delayed starts; the desire to drop by the boss's office, the list goes on, and it can feel overwhelming, right? So we won't advocate that you must do all of the things we list below *within* the first ten minutes, but we'd like you to aim to get through some (or even all) of them within the first hour of starting work.

Whilst some of these ideas may or may not chime with those other 'start-your-day-with…' lists out there, the one thing that's for sure is that the majority of the world's most successful leaders – whether we're talking Gandhi or Mandela; Mother Teresa or Pope Francis; Steve Jobs, Tim Cook and Jonny Ive at Apple, or Bill Gates at Microsoft; Jeff Bezos, CEO and Founder of Amazon; Mark Zuckerberg of Facebook; Paul Polman, CEO of Unilever; Lakshmi Mittal of ArcelorMittal; Carlos Ghosn, CEO of Renault *and* Nissan; Howard Schulz, Chairman and CEO of Starbucks; Elon Musk, the founder of Tesla motor cars and rocket makers SpaceX; whether it's Chancellor Angela Merkel, Winston Churchill, FD Roosevelt or Barack Obama; Picasso or Warhol; Gershwin or Bono; or money man Warren Buffett, the most successful investor on the planet – all start(ed) their days the same way. Whilst we certainly wish we could say that they each start their day with safety, this isn't what we're getting at. What we mean, is that each of these leaders start their day in the *same way, each day.* Their success is built – at least in part – on routine and habit, consistently applied, day in, day out.

Research shows that the most important time for creating habits is at the beginning of the day when our minds are rested, fresh and alert. So let's set the scene now to make sure you start each day *just right.* Here's our top five daily habits that we believe set great safety leaders apart and clearly demonstrate a commitment to getting things both in balance and under control.

1 **Reflect** – we know that this may sound ironic at the start of a day, but getting the best results means that you'll need to know where you've come from as well as here you're headed. Look at the progress your organization has been making in safety, review current activities or strategies and ask yourself what you can do today to move these positively forward. Remember that it's a marathon, not a sprint, and find one thing to focus on for the day ahead that will demonstrate your commitment to getting safety *just right*.

2 **Visualize success** – by now you'll have switched your mindset from preventing accidents to creating safety and focusing on the positive outcomes rather than those negative failures called incidents and injuries. So think forward to the day and week ahead and explore your role in leading the charge towards 'safety excellence', getting people 'home without harm', or whatever goal you've set. Consider the recent feedback you've received from your people and choose just one thing to do or say today that will move you forward towards your goal.

3 **Build a block** – on your journey to improving workplace safety accidents may occur. Once you've investigated fully (and proportionately) and implemented control measures you believe are practical, relevant and useful, it's time to stop thinking about the events of the past[3]. Don't dwell, instead build a mental block to draw a line under the event and prevent any negativity seeping through your brain which might throw a dark veil around your approach to improving safety. It's time to focus forward on the future now.

4 **Check the temperature** – great leaders, no matter their interests or line of work, always take the time to check in with the team, so get out

there and say 'good morning'. Your presence on the shop-floor will provide a quick boost of energy, and when you pepper your greeting with positive questions, comments and feedback about safety it also sets a tone which will engage and motivate people to work safely. The more often you are out there with them at first light, the easier it will become for you to pick up when things are a 'little off', or when there's a storm brewing, and your presence will build confidence and trust in your team which will encourage them to share their own thoughts and ideas with you. Remember, this isn't about a formal tour or inspection, it's just a quick drop in to say hi and let them know you're there, so vary your route, those you talk with and your observations each day. Remember it's all about asking questions: *"How are you?"*, *"How did things go yesterday?"*, *"What are you busy with today?"*, *"How do we make sure we do this safely?"*

5 **Open with safety** – as your first meeting of the day begins, open with time for everyone to reflect on safety. We don't mean just reviewing whether there were any incidents the day before. We mean asking the people at the meeting to reflect on whether they've learned anything important in the last few hours or days about safety. Your safety reflection may be based on something you've experienced personally – Andrew can vividly recall sitting around a boardroom table when a colleague shared the news of his own child being struck by a reversing car in the street where he lives – though it can equally be something you've picked up from the newspaper, a journal article or industry magazine. The purpose of the safety reflection time is to galvanise attention, to demonstrate that this really is a core value and to promote discussion. If it's appropriate, use humour – a great safety point we heard recently featured the leader talking about a minor accident he'd had at home changing a light fitting. Having 'forgotten' to isolate the electricity supply the shock sent him shooting across the hallway, knocking a picture off the wall and smashing a hole in a door

panel, thus creating three times the amount of Do-It-Yourself than he had originally anticipated. We know this is may feel awkward to start with, but it does get easier. Once you've established this pattern of behaviour, your team will be looking out for things in their daily lives knowing they can bring them to the meetings to share – including mistakes that they've made, learned from and are now willing to share the learnings from. Now *that's* leadership!

Leading mindfully

In his practical guide to improving safety culture, *From Accidents to Zero*, Andrew included a chapter on mindfulness. As an A to Z of all things safety culture, at first he wasn't sure that it quite fitted the concept. Though the more he explored and experimented with the concept personally in his own life, whilst at the same time noticing a lack of mindfulness in how leaders were leading safety around the globe, he became more and more convinced there was not just a place, but indeed a real need, for the topic in the book. As it turned out, not only was the mindfulness chapter well received, it was even highlighted as a 'favourite chapter' by many readers around the globe.

In such a fast-paced world where distractions appear 24/7, information flow is set permanently to 'overload' and pressure to perform is constant, running at 100 miles per hour has become the new normal and these negative factors subsumed into being just part of the job. We both know many, many leaders who tell us that they are *surviving* their jobs and lives. Surviving. Doesn't sound much like the balance is *just right* does it? We've also come across a handful of leaders who tell us that they are *thriving*. Now that's more like it! So what do these thriving leaders have in common? Do they have the smallest to-do lists? The biggest numbers of resources at their disposal? Or more capable teams? No, the single thing common to each of these leaders is their practice of mindfulness. Today, the smartest leaders are thinking mindfully. They're slowing down in order to speed up. And each tell us that not only do they get more done, more quickly, but they are more able to think outside the box, improve their focus, and feel higher levels of flexibility, agility and adaptability. In his formidable little book *One Second Ahead* Rasmus Hougaard explains:

"the new normal in business is an ever-changing, globally interconnected and competitive reality. Traditional factors of knowledge, speed and experience no longer meet the demands. In fact, today they can keep you stagnated in the status quo with a leadership style of yesterday."

Many of today's major crises in the business world seem to occur because people didn't see them coming. This is precisely what happens when people are so busy doing that they stop thinking.

Technology giant Google has been focusing on developing its leaders for several years now. Combining mindfulness techniques with advanced neuroscience and positive psychology their *'Search Inside Yourself'* program is designed to build a positive mindset and centred leadership. Google recognises that:

"Effective leadership isn't about just checking off more tasks. It's defined by how well we use our minds and interact with others. We need flexibility and clear purpose in the face of complexity… yet our workplaces are churning out burned out leaders who report little bandwidth for big-picture thinking, for innovation, truly understanding others and building strong culture."

In *Flat World Navigation* Kim Taylor-McDonald argues for a new key Performance Indicator, one where 'ROI' stands for Return on *Involvement*. What a brilliant concept! As Taylor-McDonald points out

"Sustained, authentic engagement is the best way to create a collaborative ecosystem of credibility, clarity and respect."

We totally agree!

Authentic engagement

So how to build engagement that lasts? Share the progress that your team is making on creating safety in the workplace. In a recent multi-year research study, published in the Harvard Business Review as one of the *Key Breakthrough Ideas of the Year*, Teresa Amabile and Steve Kramer articulated their findings. They discovered that when managers were asked for the number one factor that motivated people at work the answer was *'reward and recognition'*. When workers replied, their response was markedly different: *'a sense of progress'* was what they wanted.

Working with a large Russian oil business recently regarded by Bloomberg as the *'largest independent left in Russia and not connected to any group of interests'* Andrew was impressed by both their ability to produce and their leadership style. The Wall Street Journal reported that in 2015 the company had generated a 50% increase over the previous year's performance to average 120,000 barrels per day. And then they repeated the same outstanding performance in 2016, too. And all this with an admirable safety performance and visible commitment to further improvement. What's the secret? Marina, the organization's General Director begins *"we simply treat people as we expect to be treated by them: clearly setting out our expectations that everyone goes home safe everyday, and we all have a role to play in making sure that happens."* Managing Director Nicolay sagely adds *"There's no time to stop and be proud. We just get on with our work. And when people do great things, we let them know they're going in the right direction and we appreciate their efforts."*

The Russian oil company confirms Amabile and Kramer's 'Progress Principle' by proving that it's not about movie tickets, free barbecues at month end or cash bonus prizes, it's as simple as your people knowing that they're heading in the right direction – and that someone senior is watching and recognizing their work. There's no need for show-boating or for those *"1000 Days without an Accident"* signs. It's just like Aretha Franklin said, it's all about respect. Whether in the early days of change or further down the road to success, don't ever forget that a pat on the back, a wink and a smile, or a simple *"thanks for doing a good job here"* all work wonders.

So here we are. The end of the final chapter. In this section we've glued together the key points and bound them into specific thoughts, questions and suggestions for your action. But just because it's the final chapter doesn't mean that we don't have a little something extra for you. As usual, here's a few additional thoughts for you to ponder before we move to bringing this whole story to a final conclusion.

1 How would you rate levels of integrity and emotional intelligence amongst your management peer group? What can you do to help them lead forward with safety?

2 How do you feel about your own awareness of health and safety risks and controls in your workplace? Where might you need to build your knowledge?

3 We suggested taking tea with a group of your workers. Why did we do this? What might you expect from such a meeting? What are your objectives? How comfortable would you feel doing this?

4 What is your personal vision for safety in your organization? How would you articulate that in a few words?

5 How do you feel about the Golden Rules we've set out in this chapter? Which of the ten might prove most challenging to you? And how might you manage these?

6 Many of the world's greatest leaders have earned their success through employing certain daily habits to drive positive action. What small actions can you turn into daily habits to create safety?

7 How much time do you have, or make for yourself to reflect and be mindful? How could you build this into your daily routine?

8 When was the last time you thanked someone for a job well done?

Footnotes

1 Many organizations seem to think that their vision for safety is a separate and standalone document to the safety policy often required under local laws, but that's just another myth. In most jurisdictions you do need to clearly state what your health and safety policy is but there's no requirement for it to be a standalone policy statement, you can easily combine your vision statement and policy statement in one, and it makes a lot of sense too, right?

2 Sir Michael Barber is a man who knows about change. Formerly Head of the Change Delivery Unit under Tony Blair's Labour government in the United Kingdom, Barber went on to advise the Chief Minister of Pakistan's largest province on a plan to encourage more than seven million kids into schools and to raise education standards. His book *How to Run a Government So That Citizens Benefit and Taxpayers Don't Go Crazy* helped inspire these Golden Rules. A politician that gets things done. Impressive.

3 We, of course, mean this in the greatest of respect, especially where people have suffered pain or loss from a work-related accident. We're certainly not advocating you ignore and forget about injuries and suffering, but rather draw a line and look forward to avoiding recurrence by focusing on what you can do to create safety.

**This is no time for ease and comfort.
It is the time to dare and to endure.**

Winston Churchill, former Prime Minister
of Great Britain

CONCLUSION
Create Safety, Goldilocks!

With this book, we deliberately set out to create a different mindset. We are not alone, and we are certainly not the first, to say that we want safety to be seen and recognised as an integral part of everyone's job in every organization. We don't know of any employee who goes to work without wanting to go home safe and unharmed at the end of the day. After all, no one sets out to get hurt.

But we do know that in spite of this, there is also a growing tendency for people to expect others to do the thinking – and the *minding* for them. We've explored how this leads to a culture of looking for others to take responsibility – and ultimately to blame – if and when things go wrong.

One of the reasons that we both felt compelled to write this particular book, was not simply to add to the many good text books which are already out there but rather to speak directly to managers about the fundamental importance of your role and to try to fill a gap we see in the training and understanding of managers across many industry sectors around the world.

We have heard of lots of managers that wait for others to tell them what they need to do when it comes to safety. We believe it's time to change that perspective to one where being safe at work is part of the culture, where everyone knows and understands their role and where we all look after ourselves and each other. It really is as simple as that.

The real focus of this book has been on the role of the leader in creating this type of culture, by leading for, with and in safety. It is not just important, it is crucial. <u>You</u> must decide how you want to lead your business and motivate your staff. You must decide (with help and support from others) how to meet the outcome-based standards of health and safety laws that are required of your business. Safety leadership is about *minding your own business* because you care about the business and the people in it – and about sleeping soundly at night knowing you've done the right thing. Not doing it because someone else said you *had to* or by asking others to do it for you.

It's time to shift from the traditional style of workplace safety, to step away from that armour-clad construct of compliance-focused command-and-control. Management systems should be descriptive not prescriptive. The future of safety is one where leaders focus on collaboration not control. And that future is now. It is only through creating safety and getting the balance *just right* for your organization that the triple bottom line of people, planet and profit will be realized.

This really is a major leadership challenge, but we firmly believe that it is possible for everyone in a position of leadership to do it – and to do it well. You don't have to be an expert in health and safety. You do have to be good at asking questions and finding out what the challenges and the risks are. You'll need a clear vision for how you want the culture to be in your workplace and then set about inspiring others to work with you to turn that vision into a reality.

We've argued that when it comes to workplace health and safety, we've systematized so many things that people often feel processed and passed from pillar to post. We suggest that the antidote to this is realizing that it's time to reconnect with what great leadership is all about: people.

We know that one size doesn't fit all – it rarely does in any sphere but certainly not in health and safety. This is about really understanding the nature of your business, identifying the most significant risks and managing them in a way that involves and motivates the people who work for you – and that will depend on where you are in the world, the history of your business, your culture and the make-up of the workforce.

There are some cultural norms where people expect to be told what to do and where they have been conditioned throughout their lives to respect and never challenge authority. In other cultures, it may be perfectly normal to ask why you should do what anyone else tells you to, regardless of their rank. In a world of work without borders it's about getting the mix *just right*, assessing for yourself what is needed in your location with this mix of people and adapting your style of leadership to suit the context or situation. Many of the elements of what has worked for you in other places *may* be transferable but you cannot simply lift and shift or plug-and-play what has worked elsewhere without considering in which ways the people are different and how they are likely to respond to the way in which you communicate with them.

Focusing on success

Judith has spent much of her working life in the major hazards industries, where clear and positive process safety leadership is at the core of managing the business. The consequence of getting things wrong in these sectors can be catastrophic as we've illustrated with some of the examples we've referred to. In the last few years a good deal of work has been done to identify the key principles of leadership which need to be applied to process safety. The key to process safety is about anticipating what can happen and dealing with it before it happens. It really is a mindset which focuses on how to assure success because waiting for failure and then putting it right really is not an option. The UK-based Process Safety Leadership Group has identified seven key principles which we share here:

1 Process safety leadership requires board level involvement and competence

2 Good process safety management does not happen by chance and requires constant active engagement

3 Board level visibility and promotion of process safety leadership is essential to set a positive safety culture throughout the organization

4 Engagement of the workforce is needed in the promotion and achievement of good process safety management

5 Monitoring process safety performance based on both leading and lagging indicators is central to ensuring business risks are being effectively managed

6 Publication of process safety performance information provides important public assurance about the management of risks by an organization

7 Sharing best practice across industry sectors, and learning and implementing lessons from relevant incidents in other organizations, are important to maintain the currency of corporate knowledge

Although the language is slightly different from that which we have used in this book, the principles are sound and fit well with what we have been saying. We offer them here because we think that they don't just apply to process safety but to leading and managing *every* aspect of safety in every workplace when they are applied in a proportionate way. Here's why:

1 Safety must be a board level matter because it is about understanding the risks in the business and to the business. Board members do not need to be expert in health and safety but they do need to understand the risks and their responsibilities. Like we have said, members of the board need to be able to ask the right questions and be prepared and able to listen to what they are told, even when it gets uncomfortable. It is the board or senior management team's responsibility to decide what matters most, identify what is not so important, and to allocate the resources – time money, people, knowledge – where it is most needed and where it will lead to the biggest and most successful impacts for the business.

2 Safety management is dynamic and ongoing. It has to be because it is about people and it is about businesses that are changing and developing. We've talked a lot about the need for mindfulness and engagement. No paper or procedure-based management system in the world can ever 'fix' safety once and for all.

But in an organization where you have set the leadership style and where people feel valued and engaged they will be thinking about safety and offering ideas for how to make things better, not just raising concerns. You will know when you have it *just right* because the feedback from your teams will tell you that they know you care and they feel involved as opposed to feeling like they have had safety 'done to' them.

3 Leadership from the top is key – and that means *actions* not words. It means being seen to take an interest, to be caring about your workforce, to listen to concerns and committed to resolving the really serious concerns. This is not a principle which applies exclusively to process safety, it even actually applies much more broadly than to managing safety – in every workplace.

If you make promises of high bonuses or offer false hopes of a rosy future for the business which then fail to be delivered, you know that the workforce will become disillusioned and turned off. One of Judith's favourite quotations is *"I cannot hear what you say, because your actions speak a thousand times louder."* If you state that certain values are important and must be lived out in the organization, you must prove this by demonstrating those values in everything you do. If you don't, you may still be the boss in name, but you will not be regarded as a leader.

4 Safety is a team sport, no one can be a spectator. It is crucial that everyone in the workforce regardless of their rank or employment status understands their role and their responsibilities, and carries them out because they believe they are important not just to them but for the success of the business. Organizations where everyone is committed to looking out for themselves and their co-workers are ones where people want to work. We have said in this book that many of the ideas or solutions you are looking for which will lead to safety success are out there already. You just need to ask the right people in the right way, to listen to their responses, and involve them in deciding what matters most and how to make things better.

5 Measures of safety performance are important in any business but the best ones are those that tell you whether or not you are on the right track, not those that tell you when you've failed.

That means you need leading indicators that help to determine whether your leadership is setting the organization up for success.

Recall our comments about choosing and using the indicators that mean something to you and your organization. Don't fall into the trap of using indicators to make irrelevant or meaningless comparisons with other organizations which are very different from yours. Watch out for those 'Looking Good Indexes' too – meaningful indicators which help you to manage performance are what you should be seeking and reporting not ones which simply give your boss or the board members a warm glow.

6 Being open and transparent about your commitment to safety and your performance is a powerful way of telling customers, suppliers, potential employees, neighbours, shareholders and others about your business. Who wouldn't want to work for an organization that makes clear that it really cares about the safety of its employees?

How you make that information public depends very much on your business and who your most important stakeholders are. Major hazard industries in many parts of the world are required to report publicly on their performance. In any business you will need to make an external report when someone is hurt – to the regulator, to your insurer, to the family and others. What we have tried to do in this book is to get you to consider how you can demonstrate your enthusiasm for safety by sharing that with others. Why would you keep that just within the boundary fence of your organization? Your communication does, of course, need to come from the heart and it has to be authentic. Say what you mean and what you believe and you will inspire others.

7 Learning every lesson the hard way from your own painful experience

is inefficient and costly, in more ways than one. Sharing knowledge and learning from others about what works and what doesn't is essential to getting it right in your company. Though take care – as we have said several times don't just try to plug-and-play! The solutions and ideas you pick up that have worked for others will likely need sense-checking and refinement before being introduced in your business.

Learning from others' mistakes is just as important, though it does require an level of open-mindedness. Don't focus on the detail – the widget that failed, the mistake an individual made – remember the need to get to root causes, to understand what really went wrong and ask *why?, why?, why?, why?, why?*. Only then you will be starting to apply the learning in a mindful and constructive way in your own organization, rather than falling into the trap of convincing yourself that what went wrong there can't or won't happen in your business because your place is different.

So, it seems to us that the seven key principles of process safety leadership are pretty much on the same track as we are. It may be said in a different way, but that's ok. The leaders in that industry are saying it in a way that works for them. Now it's your turn.

A culture of obsession

André Spicer, Professor of Organizational Behaviour at Cass Business School, City University, London and founder of the ETHOS: The Centre for Responsible Enterprise well describes modern organizational culture when he says:

"In Anglo-Saxon style companies where people are coming and going more, people are promoted on delivery – I can deliver stuff, I can get things

done. And often they become obsessed with getting things done rather than questioning <u>how</u> they get things done."

Spicer talks of an unsustainable culture based on short term perspectives and we know of many companies where this philosophy has prevailed, in fact we've shared some examples of them in this book. We have also exposed just how high the stakes are in taking this approach. If you're lucky, bad things won't happen – at least not on your watch – but luck is not a good basis on which to run any business. We are very much in favour of creating a long-term sustainable culture where everyone knows that their role and the leadership is *just right* – a culture where no one is tempted to bend the rules even just once. That means digging deep, understanding well and asking questions – of ourselves as leaders, and of those around us.

Good business is good safety

The theme running through everything we're saying in this book is that the solution to creating a great culture of safety, first and foremost, is good business practice. Knowing that from the top of an organization down and creating and sustaining a culture that understands risks and benefits across all relevant issues will maintain and enhance success whilst at the same time avoid the risk of shaky foundations that could, as BP, DuPont and many more industrial greats have found, see it literally all blow up around them.

The core principle of health and safety management in the United Kingdom are that those who create risks are best placed to control those risks. And involving businesses and other relevant organizations not only helps with getting things right, it helps in gaining buy-in and commitment. Modern health and safety regulation in the UK dates back over 40 years now, to the Health and Safety at Work Act in 1974 and the setting up of the Health and Safety Executive the following year. But one of the reasons that the UK has one of the best health and safety records in the world is that the system is constantly learning and evolving. The principles stay the same but how they are applied to new and emerging technologies and risks adapts and changes with the times. Here again we see that dynamic approach of never sitting back and seeing 'job done' but constantly learning and adapting. There's a lot to commend the approach – whichever country you are in around the world.

Principles of success

We expect that there will be some people who read this book who will say that we are being too simplistic in our approach, that health and safety is much more complex than we make it out to be. But we would question the motivation of those who do that. It is very clear to us that layers of complexity have built up around health and safety in many organizations, but we will continue to ask 'Why is that?' We've talked about some of the fear that lies behind this behaviour – fear of civil litigation, fear of failure, fear of laws which don't actually exist and how all this leads to to risk averse behaviour.

We firmly believe that there is a great opportunity waiting to be taken which will make your business more successful and more sustainable, and most importantly of all it's not difficult. At least, it isn't difficult if you are able to see the benefits it will bring and the fact that your role in it is to lead and inspire others, not to become the health and safety expert.

We think that of the many principles of health and safety leadership which we have described here, the very notion of leading for success is the one which needs to be considered and applied more broadly. Just as those principles of process safety leadership translate to wider health and safety management, so let's take one last look at them in an even bigger context.

- **Leadership requires board level involvement and competence.** The very best companies are led by strong leadership teams who have a good handle on all aspects of the business – including health and safety. If health and safety is an integral part of the full suite of issues that the leadership team focuses on they will be making good decisions about priorities and addressing the most important topics, dynamically as the business grows.

- **Good management does not happen by chance and requires constant active engagement**. Good companies identify and develop their leaders. They provide training, coaching, mentoring. In a rapidly changing world those skills and abilities need to be updated and refreshed – no one waits and hopes that it will happen by chance.

- **Board level visibility and promotion of leadership is essential to set a positive culture throughout the organization.** No-one likes working for an organization where the board and the top leaders are invisible. Motivation and commitment grow when the leaders are seen and heard out in the business, and when they listen to the views of staff.

- **Engagement of the workforce is needed in the promotion and achievement of good management**. If leaders are visible and engaging the workforce will engage and results will be delivered because they feel part of the team.

- **Monitoring performance based on both leading and lagging indicators is central to ensuring business risks are being effectively managed**. Whoever heard of a successful business which measured itself simply by looking backwards at what it had already done? Successful and sustainable businesses know where they want to go, they have a vision and a plan and they measure their performance to make sure that they are on track to succeed. They don't wait to fail before they review their performance, they look for ways to do even better and create success every day.

- **Publication of performance information provides important public assurance about the management of risks by an organization**. In many companies shareholders and stakeholders expect this information. In fact there are legal requirements around what must be reported annually but the best companies don't stick to just reporting what is required by law, they provide more information about their culture and their values because they know it is an important differentiator for shareholders and potential future employees and customers.

- **Sharing best practice across industry sectors, and learning and implementing lessons from relevant incidents in other organizations, are important to maintain the currency of corporate knowledge.** The smartest businesses are not afraid to copy good practice when they see it. If it works for others and can be applied in their business, why wait? Recruitment of staff from other organizations is often driven by wanting to bring in corporate knowledge which has driven success elsewhere.

So there you have it. The conclusion of this book is that managing and leading workplace health and safety is an integral part of being a good manager and a good leader. These same principles apply to managing every dimension of the business. By not applying the principles to any one aspect of your business – whether that is health and safety, marketing, finance or anything else – then the gap begins to widen and you are unlikely to be truly leading for success and fully minding your own business.

We hope that you enjoyed reading this book and reflecting on the questions we've posed within these pages. We also hope that together they have inspired you to look at your own personal suite of leadership skills and whether you have a gap in the spectrum when it comes to leading on health and safety. It really is your business and we hope we have inspired you to *mind your own business* and get things *just right* in the very best and broadest sense. We wish you success, *Goldilocks*, keep *creating safety*!

To give real service you must add something which cannot be bought or measured with money, and that is sincerity and integrity.

Douglas Adams, Author of *The Hitchhiker's Guide to the Galaxy*

About the Authors

Dame Judith Hackitt's engineering background spans many years as a frontline manager in high hazard industries where health and safety simply could not be added on – it was integral to everyone's role in the organization. For Judith it has been hard to understand how other organizations failed to get this from the start and somehow ended up in a place where safety was about paperwork and bureaucracy and worse still, waiting for someone else to tell the boss what to do – be that the health and safety manager, the consultant or the regulator.

When Judith moved out of industry in 2007 to take on the role of Chair of Great Britain's Health and Safety Executive ('HSE') this marked the start of a mission to put safety ownership back where it belonged – in the hands of those who create the risks in the first place – and to draw a clear distinction between the stuff that really matters – because it threatens life and limb – and the ever increasing waves of trivia and bureaucracy which was getting in the way.

Throughout her tenure as Chair of HSE, Judith devoted herself to repositioning ownership of safety, to calling for common sense and proportionality and above all for leaders to recognise that this is as much a part of their job as monitoring financial profit and loss.

In December 2015 Judith was awarded the honour of becoming a

Dame for her services to health and safety and for being a role model for Engineers. Now Chair of EEF, The Manufacturing Organization in the UK, she sees even more clearly the need to link good practice in health and safety with delivering productivity and business success.

Professor Andrew Sharman also started his working life in engineering – after all, safety just wasn't very cool back in the early 1990s. A chance encounter with a bucket of acid was the epiphany that changed his view – and his career. After almost two decades of leading safety for large multinational organizations Andrew founded a consulting business, based in Switzerland, specializing in improving culture and enabling excellence for Non-Governmental Organizations, FTSE 100 and Fortune 500 corporations around the world through industry sectors as diverse as mining, aviation, construction, oil and gas, pharmaceuticals, retail and fast-moving consumer goods.

Andrew is a Professor of Leadership & Safety Culture at CEDEP, the Centre for Executive Development at Fontainebleau, France and Visiting Professor in Work & Wellbeing at the University of Zurich, Switzerland. Holding Masters degrees in Organizational Behaviour and International Health & Safety Law he is proud to be a Chartered Fellow of the Institution of Occupational Safety & Health (IOSH), a Fellow of the International Institute of Risk and Safety Management (IIRSM), a Fellow of the Institute of Leadership & Management, and a Fellow of the Institute of Directors.

An advocate for thinking differently and repositioning the practice and profession of safety as a business enabler, Andrew has authored 4 books, over 300 journal articles and given over 200 conference papers on the topics of safety behaviour, organizational culture and leadership around the world. He has held Non-Executive Directorships on the boards of several NGOs including the Earth Focus Foundation, and as Vice Chairman of the board of IOSH, the world's leading body for health and safety professionals for whom he currently serves in the capacity of Vice President.

Far from being risk-averse, he loves adventure sports including climbing, free flying, sea kayaking, and, most of all, swimming with sharks. Check out his TED talk to find out how he does that safely.

All men's gains are the fruit of venturing.

Heredotus, Greek Historian

Further Reading

This book has been shaped by our own experiences in workplace health and safety over many years.

We believe that the answers to many of the challenges and frustrations leaders face today can often be found by looking beyond the discipline. Here's a few suggestions for further reading which might help you get your culture *just right*.

More Human – Steve Hilton

Viral Change – Leandro Herrero

Black Box Thinking – Matthew Syed

The Light and Fast Organization – Patrick Hollingworth

Subliminal – Leonard Mlodlnow

The Feeling of Risk – Paul Slovic

Have a question?

Thanks for reading this book, we hope that you've found it useful and are already making good progress in creating safety and getting your workplace safety culture *just right*.

If you've got a question or a comment drop us a line at ads@andrewsharman.com - we'd love to hear from you.

From Accidents to Zero
A Practical Guide to Improving Your Workplace Safety Culture

Combining positive psychology and organizational behaviour with proven safety methodology, binding together the most influential research with vast international experience into a clear guide for action.

Whether you're an operational manager or a safety specialist, From Accidents to Zero provokes thought and provides pragmatic guidance from the very first page. The book demystifies health & safety culture and features over 80 new ideas that will not only reduce accidents but will also save lives.

"An eminently practical knowledge toolbox filled with tools which will add great value to the CEO, department managers and front-line safety practitioners in equal measures. Relevant, accessible and applicable, this is 'safety distilled' and a must-read."
Steven Brown, Brewery Manager, Heineken

"From the Jedi Master of safety leadership comes a powerfully positive book that points us towards what we can do to really make a difference. Blending out-of-the-box thinking with human applications and psychology this book will transform your safety change effort. Truly stellar."
Steve Giblin, Speedy Services

Visit **www.fromaccidentstozero.com** and enter code
MIND25 for **25% discount** on your copy

Safety Savvy
What You Need to Know to Stay Alive Longer in a Dangerous and Uncertain World

The pressure to be safe and healthy is stronger now than it's ever been. The response to this is usually more policies, more procedures and more checklists. But is this really the answer? Providing a refreshing antidote to the rules-based bureaucracy and with contributions from Brad Pitt, Tom Cruise, Nelson Mandela, Dirty Harry and Rocky Balboa this spicy little book shares the five truths of the *Safety Savvy* in a way that will change your view of safety forever.

"This book takes famous movie quotes and cleverly relates them to situations in society which have an impact on health and safety, giving it a really broad appeal. Fits snugly inside your back pocket - ideal to pull out when sitting on the bus, waiting for a train or just relaxing down the pub. In fact, it's written in a style that feels like the authors are chatting to you over a pint, asking you, the reader, the questions, making it highly thought-provoking."
SHP magazine

"An excellent read with fundamental truths that will jolt your mind back to the reality of everyday safety hazards - the obvious and the not so obvious ones. Even the most astute out there will learn a thing or two from this read which offers a pragmatic perspective on the everyday complexities around safety."
Deon Van Tonder, H&S Manager, Aveng Grinaker-LTA

Visit **www.fromaccidentstozero.com** and enter code MIND25 for **25% discount** on your copy

A new type of thinking is essential if mankind is to survive and move towards higher levels.

Albert Einstein, Physicist

Training Courses

The Missing MBA Safety Module

You've read the book, now it's time to take action and join the authors on the program!

You've learned that it's time to step away from the armour-clad construct of compliance-focused rules and systems.

You understand that the future of workplace safety is one where great leaders think differently and focus personally on engagement, empowerment and collaboration. And you know that this future starts *now. But how do you get started?*

The **Mind Your Own Business MBA Safety Module** is an inspiring, action-focused program for modern leaders striving to regain a sense of balance when it comes to workplace health and safety and fill that gap for those who have already completed their MBA program.

Building on the concepts in this book, you'll learn tools and techniques that will help you get the balance *just right* for your organization and create a **Personal Leadership Plan** to *mind your own business* and lead your organization to success.

The three-day program will help you to:

- Explore the culture in your own organization and understand the factors that *really* drive that culture

- Identify what's currently getting in the way of performance improvement, cultural maturity, and your leadership

- Envision a new future where safety and success go hand-in-hand and the balance is *just right*

- Build confidence in your ability to be an authentic safety leader

- Identify the *real* 'movers and shakers' in your organization who can support you on the journey – and those who might be holding you back

- Develop an action plan to deliver sustainable results in the new paradigm

This program is delivered exclusively by Andrew Sharman and Judith Hackitt through face-to-face workshops in small groups and individual one-to-one coaching, as the authors act as your personal guides and mentors to help you lead and manage safety efficiently, effectively and with impact whilst building shared accountability and measurable improvement both in health and safety performance and organizational culture.

Don't put it off! If this book has inspired you to lead on safety, email us now at **info@fromaccidentstozero.com** to find out more about working with Andrew and Judith on the ***Mind Your Own Business*** program in your organization, now.

Total Safety Leadership

The **Total Safety Leadership** program is a two-day masterclass for operational leaders and managers who want to make a difference in the way they lead with safety and forward-focused safety practitioners who are ready to think differently.

Based on the global best-selling book on safety culture **From Accidents to Zero** this masterclass is dynamic, fast-paced and highly interactive as participants explore key aspects of workplace culture from employee engagement and motivation, to risk-taking behaviour, affective communication and high-impact leadership.

Total Safety Leadership is approved by the **International Institute of Risk and Safety Management.** Participants receive an IIRSM certificate on completion of the program.

Thousands of leaders from around the world have used the program to dramatically shift performance, improve culture and enable excellence in their organizations. Here's what they have to say about it:

"Bright ideas delivered in a simple, straight-forward way, so that they went straight to our heads and to our hearts. We all know that rules and procedures are very important to build a robust safety culture, but Total Safety Leadership makes it clear that we also need to pay great attention to what people think and feel about safety. This program has significantly influenced my personal leadership style, in this regard let me express my gratitude to you once again."
Chief Executive Officer, Oil & Gas industry

"An inspiring masterclass – the most impactful safety event I ever attended and now I have a zillion ideas on what I want to do differently to improve safety culture in my business."
Global Director, Chemicals industry

"An fantastic program that really got me thinking about how I lead safety at work. The interactive approach brought several 'a-ha!' moments for me."
Operations Director, Automotive industry

"The energy in this program is contagious and the approach defies convention, breathing new life into what can be perceived as dry subject matter. Excellent!"
Department Head, FMCG industry

Email **info@fromaccidentstozero.com** to find out more about running the *Total Safety Leadership* program in your organization.

Notes

Notes

Notes

Notes

Notes